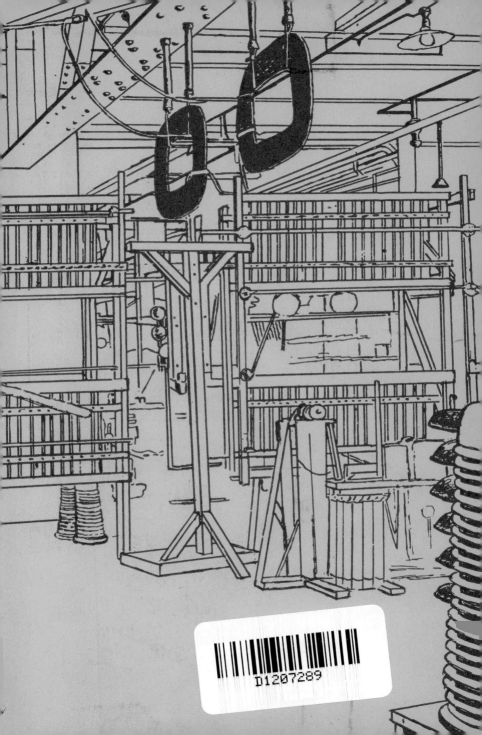

# AMERICAN HERITAGE SERIES

# AMERICAN HERITAGE SERIES (Cont'd)

# *The* Little Giant *of* Schenectady

(( A Story of Charles Steinmetz ))

by DOROTHY MARKEY

*Illustrated by E. Harper Johnson*

ALADDIN BOOKS
*New York: 1956*

The author is grateful to Joseph Steinmetz Hayden, the scientist's grandson, for many of the illuminating details of Steinmetz' life with his adopted family.

# Contents

# Two for One

**CARL STEINMETZ MOVED ABOUT** quietly in the darkness, trying not to waken his roommate. After he had shifted his drawing board and telescope over by a window, he leaned out for a good look at the sky. The moon was down. Above the Alps, the stars were more clear than usual.

Placing the oil lamp on a nearby stand, Carl settled down to his work. He had a long night ahead, making notes while the earth turned and the stars took their course. Then he could finish his article tomorrow.

9

The editor would pay him and they would catch up on the rent.

Carl smiled as he bent over his chart, remembering his roommate's face when they had to dodge past their landlady on the stairs. Oscar had looked as if they had met up with a ghost.

When the sky began to lighten and the stars to fade, Carl put aside his telescope. Limping slightly, he took his papers over to the worktable.

The attic room was so small that he had to squeeze past his roommate's cot. Oscar Asmussen woke with a start, then seeing that dawn had not yet come he settled back under the covers. Drowsily he watched Carl at work.

"The silly goose," Oscar said to himself . . . "Once again he has forgotten sleep. And he has let the fire go out. His hands and whole body look stiff with cold." With an impatient sigh, Oscar dragged a blanket from his cot and put it around his friend.

As he felt the blanket lifted gently over the hump on his back, Carl glanced up. "Orion put on quite a show tonight. Too bad you missed it."

He pulled the blanket gratefully over his

knees. He was long-legged and well built except for his back. Only rarely did he think of himself as a cripple. He could out-walk anyone. It was always Oscar who was ready to turn back when they hiked through the fields and woods after class.

It was growing lighter in the room. Oscar made the fire, then scraped the last cocoa from a tin and put on the kettle. He turned the breadbox on its side and fished out two stale buns.

"You are noisy as a crow." With a grin Carl put aside his work, to make room on the table for the food. "And never mind, we won't starve."

Oscar sat down opposite him. "Right in math class I begin thinking: X equals two cheese buns, Y, a sausage." He stared gloomily at Zurich's pointed slate roofs. "If my uncle had sent my allowance on time, we wouldn't be in this fix."

"Oh, stop worrying! Mail from America is slow." Carl was listening to the chatter of birds under the eaves. He began crumbling up part of his roll to feed them.

"Uncle Josef never held up my check before," Oscar said. "It's three weeks overdue."

"Maybe the Old Bear is still angry with

you because of Louisa." Carl took a handful of crumbs over to the window. Just outside a pair of linnets had a nest. "Come have a look, Oscar. The young ones are sprouting feathers."

They watched the early sun breaking through the mist rising from the valley. From the street below, came sounds of vegetable and fruit sellers bumping their wooden handcarts over the cobblestones to market. The old lady across the way was already scrubbing her front steps, singing as she scrubbed.

Although the steep, little street had been home to them for almost a year, the scene from their attic window was always a fresh delight. It was different from anything either of them had known. Oscar had spent his boyhood in the raw, sprawling, American city of Los Angeles; Carl in the war-like Germany of Prime Minister Bismarck. Both boys had come to love the ancient and peaceful Swiss town.

Carl looked northeast, toward his home city of Breslau. His father would be on his way now to work in the railroad shop. Only last week he had written: *My Son, it is unwise for you to come home to Germany, even for a visit.*

Bismarck had not forgotten Carl's part in the student movement against war. For writing a leaflet against the ever-present Prussian military, he had had to go into exile. He was glad he had stood up for what was right, but he longed to see his people.

Coming back to the table, he gathered up his papers. "Oscar, any day, now, you'll get your check. In the meantime—" he flourished his pen and sat down again to work — "when the editor pays me, we celebrate."

His friend laughed, for he knew that with Carl any excuse was good for a party. There was no more talk, only the scratching of Carl's pen. Quietly, Oscar gathered his books together and set out for an early class at the Polytechnic School.

On the way, he kept thinking of the first of Carl's "celebrations," when the Fall Term had just started. Young Steinmetz was living in a basement room in the big student boardinghouse near the school. He had gone from door to door inviting as many of his classmates as he could crowd into his dark little room for supper.

All through the gay evening Oscar had wondered about the hunchback with keen, searching eyes and a handclasp that belied his slight body.  His clothes were shabby and his room, poor and bare; yet he had set out a lavish spread.  And of all the students, he seemed most alive.

After they became friends, Carl confessed that he had used up his week's funds on the party and had to live on leftovers until he could earn more.  It was worth it, he said, for he was celebrating his escape across the border to Switzerland.

How could this crippled boy have dared to stand up to Bismarck, the Goliath?  Of course, he had not been alone in his protests against turning Germany into an armed camp.  There had been strong feeling among the majority of the scholars at the University of Breslau; but Carl had written the leaflets in protest . . .

When they had become roommates, Oscar no longer found it hard to understand Carl Steinmetz' reckless courage.  With all his gaiety and humor, the boy had never failed to stand up for the things he believed in.

As he passed the town clock, Oscar saw the hands pointed to eight and he quickened his step.  He was going several blocks out of his way to pass the home of Louisa Bergson.

She waved to him from an upstairs window. Lifting his cap, he waved it sideways as a signal to let her know he still had no answer from his uncle. Then he hurried on to his class.

The sun was high over the Alps when the last lecture of the morning was finished. Shading his eyes, Oscar looked up at the white peaks glowing in the sun; then he headed for the post office.

It was much later before he started home. He took the winding stairs to the attic in long strides, calling overhead, "The letter, it's here!"

He looked up the deep stairwell, hoping his roommate would come out on the landing. Halfway up, he called out again. There was no answer. His pace slowed, since, plainly, Carl was not home.

In the empty room he saw an astronomy chart propped on the washstand. This was a signal that Carl had gone to the editor's with his article. Oscar dropped his letter on the table. At least it wasn't a math book Carl had left! When he was off tutoring fellow students he always left an open math book. Tutoring often kept him out until midnight.

Stepping over books and papers scattered over the floor, Oscar walked over to the low

dormer window. The fields between the back of the house and the mountains were bright with yellow buttercups and blue cornflowers. As he watched, the shadows of clouds passed over the fields making a beautiful pattern of lights and shadows.

It was Carl who had taught him to enjoy such things in nature. Until he knew Carl, Oscar had never had anyone he felt close to. Now their companionship was coming to an end.

Oscar pulled his uncle's letter from his pocket and read the closing paragraph once more: *I have stopped your allowance. Enclosed is your final check and your return passage to the States.*

He spread the long ticket on their worktable and examined it, trying to plan what he must do. He really had no other home than his uncle's. He scarcely remembered his parents or any other life in Denmark—after all, he was only five when they died. Strangers had brought him across the ocean to be cared for by the uncle in Los Angeles. His uncle had given him a home more out of duty than of love. Josef Asmussen was too taken up with business to have time for a growing boy.

It had been a lonely time. Neither at school nor at the California college where he had studied engineering had he made any close friendships. This final year's study abroad had been his uncle's idea; for that, at least, he would always be grateful.

Oscar glanced about the attic, barely large enough for the table and the cots and the bookshelves they had built in a corner. Once he would have thought this a shabby place, but living here with Carl Steinmetz had changed many of his ideas. Suddenly his blue eyes cleared. He folded the steamship ticket and put it back in his pocket. He had a plan if it only would work!

Restless for his friend's return, Oscar began gathering up Carl's notebooks and stacking them on his shelf. He leafed through a mathematics book. When it came to math, young Steinmetz was a genius. Everyone said so. Problems that took the rest of them several hours, he solved in his head. But Carl was matter-of-fact about his talent and didn't like a fuss. He never wanted to be thought different.

As Oscar cleared the floor of papers, he kept thinking how Carl had enjoyed their search for this place. The first night he had sat at the worktable writing his father: *I have a roommate! We live on the top floor of the last house on the last street in Zurich. It is quite reasonable. And what a view of the Alps!*

For Carl, as for him, this attic was home. If I must leave here, Oscar promised himself, I won't go without him.

He heard an uneven step on the landing and a familiar whistle.

"Light the kettle!" Carl waved a fragrant package. "Sausage and fresh buns! And the rent money!" He emptied his pocket of coins, then sat down on the cot by Oscar. "You are too quiet. Did you get news?"

Oscar nodded, his face partly hidden. He did not know how to tell Carl.

"I take it the Old Bear is still growling? He won't give in to your marrying Louisa?" Carl glanced up at the picture over his friend's cot. This girl with the heavy braids coiled about her head seemed to be smiling back at him. Oscar was lucky. "If only your uncle could know Louisa!"

Why didn't Oscar read the letter? "I don't understand your uncle. Louisa is gentle and clever. Why is he so set against her?"

Oscar flushed. "I owe Uncle Josef a lot.

He gave me the schooling he promised, and more. But he's driven himself all his life for one thing—to get ahead. It has done something to him. He never married. I don't think he's ever loved anyone. All he knows or cares about is success. He measures people, everything by it. He expects me to. Louisa's father is poor."

"Maybe you had rather not talk about it," Carl said.

"But I must talk about it. I can't go back to his way of living." Oscar unfolded the letter and flattened it out between his hands.

Carl waited for him to go on.

"You and I know the Bergsons as fine people. To my uncle they are nobodies. They just make clocks." Oscar glanced around at his companion. "I am twenty-two, but Uncle Josef has the old-fashioned idea that he can pick out a girl for me. His business partner's daughter. That marriage would be useful to him!"

At Carl's amazed look Oscar unbent, and the attic was filled with their laughter.

"Poor, deluded old man." Spent with laughing, Carl watched his roommate slowly tear up the letter and drop the pieces into a wastebasket.

"What will you do now? Maybe you will stay on here?" he said eagerly. In another month their course would be finished. They'd find jobs and Oscar could save up enough to be married.

"There is no future for me here," Oscar said. "Louisa and I talked it over with her people. I must go to America and find work."

Carl moved quickly over by the window. Oscar was leaving. It had to come, but not this soon.

"I am going to New York and get settled in a job," Oscar went on. "Then Louisa will join me. We decided everything this afternoon."

"I am happy for you, Oscar." Carl spoke from over his shoulder. "For both of you. How soon will you go?"

Oscar ignored the interruption. "And you will be best man at our wedding," he said.

Carl's smile was wistful. "With the ocean between us?"

Oscar took out the steamship ticket and waved it above his head. "See this? A first class passage to New York. I'm exchanging it for a pair of tickets in the steerage."

"But I don't understand. You said Louisa was coming later."

"The other steerage passenger will be you."

Carl looked toward the mountains, yet hardly seeing them. Beyond their heights lay a magic land stretching from the Atlantic to the Pacific. Since he was a little boy, he had dreamed of going to America. The year he was born, that very year, the American Civil War had ended. Friends of his father had been soldiers in that war to free the great nation of the blot of slavery. Such a wonderful country, with so many opportunities!

While he was still a youngster, letters had come back full of the marvelous new things happening in the United States. Railroads spanning the continent . . . huge cities rising . . . factories . . . bridges! Only a few years ago, in 1883, the German newspapers had printed pictures of electric lights on Brooklyn Bridge—the great bridge designed by a German immigrant.

And then there were the stories his grandmother used to tell him of the endless wilderness peopled by the American pioneers, of the flatboats on the Great Father of Waters, of Indian tribes. No doubt some of the things were fairy tales but they glowed in his memory.

And many of the University students,

exiled like himself because of the struggle against the policies of Bismarck, had taken ship for America. Every boat crossing the Atlantic was crowded—not from Germany alone but from every country in Europe. With so many new inhabitants, with so much building, there was bound to be a great chance for scientists and engineers.

"Carl, think of the exciting work we can do together."

His friend's words seemed to come from far off. "My father said in your country you have freedom and work for all. A 'Land of Brothers.' Is it true, Oscar? And so vast— surely a land made for giants." Carl looked down at his dwarfed body. "No, hardly for me," he said quietly.

He had thought he was done with the bitter knowledge his playmates had brought him. He was six when he first heard it from them. They had been sailing boats along a flooded street gutter in Breslau when a boy said, "Let's choose up sides for a game of ball." Carl was left out.

"Choose me!" he begged, but they told him, "Not on our side." He ran to the other side, but they did not want him either. . . .

Since that day he had learned to live with

his crippled back, even to forget it. Now the old pain had taken hold of him, and the doubt. America was not for a cripple — a hunchback.

Oscar had never heard Carl speak of his deformity before. When Carl began scribbling out algebra equations on a paper, he sighed. He knew that habit of his roommate's when he was thinking hard.

"Give me a year," Carl said. "Maybe two. We'll see." It was true he could not return to Germany and there was little for him here in Switzerland. And in America they were doing big things with motors. And with electricity.

"Why not come now? It will be much easier for you if you come now, Carl. Besides, I need you."

Carl was still busy with his equations. "You know I have no money," he said, without looking up.

"We believe in share-and-share-alike, remember? With the ticket and this check I've enough for both of us to cross the ocean and to eat while we look for jobs. If you want, you can pay me back later."

Carl's pencil was moving rapidly. "How can we be sure I'll get a job so fast? I can't even speak English." He was not going to mention his other reason, but he wished he could talk now with his father about it. His father, too, had a hump on his back. *"Don't think you can run away from it, son."* Carl could hear his father, as plainly as if he stood right by him. *"Go ahead and live."*

Oscar pressed his friend's shoulder. "Look how easily you picked up French, here, among the Swiss. A Greek and Latin scholar like you—why, I'll teach you English in the eight days aboard ship."

"I see you have everything worked out!" Laughing with excitement, Carl threw down his pencil. "How can I refuse?"

Oscar seized him by the hands and they spun about the room, knocking against cots and table. "This calls for a celebration!" Oscar said. "This party will be on me!"

## The Lady with the Lamp

◗ THE WIND WAS RISING AND THE
French liner *La Champagne* rolled heavily.
Carl took a firmer grip on the ship's railing.
"Tomorrow we reach America! Put a red star
around the date on the calendar: June 1,
1889."

"Do come below!" Oscar could not re-
spond to his friend's gaiety. For seven days
and nights this steamboat had been pitching
them about. And the rougher it grew, the
more Carl seemed to like it.

"There is going to be quite a storm."
Carl's eyes sparkled. "Why not stay on deck

26

and watch?" He stepped nearer, for it was
hard to talk against the wind. "Tell me once
more the right way to say it—'I speak few
English'?"

"Not few — little." Oscar saw his friend
frown. "Never mind. Once in New York
you will learn fast."

"First I must pass the examination at the
docks. Tomorrow." Before they would let
him in the country, Carl knew he must prove
able to support himself and make a good
citizen. But how could he talk to them?
Those officials would ask questions in English
and expect him to answer in their tongue.

"I'll be right there—we'll manager." Oscar
was having trouble keeping on his feet. The
ship pitched more violently, as the storm
reached its height. "For now, I'm going to
my bunk."

"You would be better off here in the open
air." Carl pulled his student's cap forward,
and lifted his head. He liked to feel the bite
of the salty spray on his face. "Portholes in
the steerage are closed. You'll feel less seasick
in the open air."

But Oscar had already departed. Carl
stood alone by the rail, watching the sky
darken and lightning flash above the angry

ocean. What power nature had! But she was wasteful of her energies. Power must be harnessed to be useful to man.

Most passengers had left the deck but near Carl a woman and boy were sitting under shelter.

"Maybe they won't let us into America?" young Pierre whispered to his mother. He had been listening to talk among the passengers with some of the crew. They had told of immigrants being sent back to Europe. "The officials would not let them in," he said.

"Did they say why?"

"Because they were sickly. Or they had no money. Every trip, Mama, some are turned back." The boy's anxious look had fixed on her calm face. "Are you *sure* they will take us?"

"But of course, Pierre! Didn't your Uncle Victor write urging us to come? You'll see. Tomorrow he will be waiting on the dock to meet us."

"There are so many on this boat," Pierre said. It was only the steerage passengers—the immigrants—he was thinking of. He had scarely seen the first class passengers on the upper deck.

Pierre's mother took his hand. "Your

father is strong and willing. They tell us America has need of such men. Oh yes, Pierre, we can be sure of a welcome."

"All of us?" The boy pointed toward the lone figure by the railing. The first night out, when he could not sleep, this young man had taken him on deck. He had pointed out the North Star and Dipper and told him how the stars helped guide sailors across the ocean. All through the voyage he had been like an old friend.

As Carl moved with a brisk limp further along the deck, Pierre asked softly, "Him, too, Mama? Are you sure?"

Marie Lefrak's glance faltered. "About him, who can say? He is young, and so kind."

"And smart, Mama!" Pierre could not bear to think of his new friend being turned back. "Maybe he's not so strong as Papa. But they will let him in, even if he is—different?"

Marie Lefrak had watched the young German hunchback. It was clear that he did not think of himself as different. Among the passengers he asked no favors but took his deformity in a matter-of-fact way that made it easy for others to do the same.

"What people remember about him is not

his crooked back and his small stature, Pierre, but other things. His gentle manner. His eyes, that miss nothing."

As the gale swept down on the liner, Pierre's mother took him inside. She glanced at Carl uneasily; but if he had overheard Pierre, he gave no sign.

Now Carl was alone on deck. He was drenched but he did not feel the downpour. He was following the storm as it increased in fury. As lightning flashed from sky to ocean, he asked himself the cause of these gigantic outbursts. And how was it that clouds stored up these electric charges in the first place? What made the lightning dart one place and not another? He felt a deep longing to understand the forces in lightning—really understand.

Benjamin Franklin and his experiment with kite and housekey had been one of the first stories he heard about America. Franklin had proven lightning to be a gigantic electric discharge. But in Franklin's day and for so long afterward electricity had been no more than a curiosity. People had marveled when they found shocks could come from a magical Leyden jar. They had marveled still more when it was discovered that currents of electricity could be sent along wires — could actually be put to use in the electric telegraph of Samuel Morse. And then had come the telephone . . .

Now, suddenly, in Carl's own lifetime the whole world had come to realize that electricity held a mighty power which, harnessed, could do much of the drudgery for mankind.

Carl had studied the discoveries of Farraday and Volt and Ampere and Clark Maxwell— the Englishman who proved that electrical magnetic effects traveled by waves. And articles about the work of living scientists were printed in all the German magazines.

When Carl was still a schoolboy his father had gone to France to the Paris Exposition and seen, with his own eyes, a train running on a mile of track. It had a small locomotive and three cars holding twenty people—and all pulled by electricity.

"The little steam train I made you is already out of date," his father had said when he came home from Paris.

But things had not gone so fast. Trains still ran by steam just like the little model Carl had in his trunk down below. Much had been discovered about electricity; much more lay in the great unknown.

As he watched the lightning flash from sky to ocean, Carl ached to widen the boundaries of knowledge. Someday, somebody would duplicate nature's lightning . . .

It seemed a crazy dream that an exile from his own country—a cripple, and penniless—would ever have the chance to make his life count in this way. On the other hand, in the matter of putting electric power to use, America was beginning to take the lead. Wasn't the whole world talking about the American, Thomas Edison, and his electric lights? About American motors? In a new country many things were possible . . .

Whistling a familiar tune, Carl went below to change into dry clothes.

Pierre ran over to him. "Remember your promise?"

Nodding, Carl pulled his trunk out from under the bunk and removed an old-fashioned sturdy chest, painted red.

"Do hurry! What all is inside?"

"Things I treasure." Smiling to himself, Carl unfastened the lock. On top of the chest were his University notebooks, bound in leather by his father. He set them aside.

Pierre was losing patience. "The train! I want to see your train!"

Carl unwound the cloth protecting the tiny model and set it down between them. "I was smaller than you, Pierre, when my father made it for me. A power-driven toy in 1870 was a rare sight. This one goes by steam. Now there are cars with motors run by electricity. Not just models, but real cars."

The ship was still ploughing through rough seas when Pierre fell asleep. Carl found he was too excited to close his eyes and before light he was back on deck. Soon he was joined by other immigrants waiting for their first glimpse of the New World.

From the crow's-nest high above them came the lookout's faint cry, "Land sighted!" Carl ran to get Oscar and they stood by the crowded rail watching for the first outline of land to appear. Nearby, Pierre jumped up and down, as if to help the ship move faster.

"Take care, please! Stand back!" Crewmen warned, as a small tender came alongside to let the pilot come aboard. He would guide the ocean liner into New York's harbor. For a moment the eyes of the immigrants were fastened on the harbor pilot as he stalked importantly past, to the upper deck.

"Look!" Pierre stopped his jumping to point overhead. Out of the early fog appeared the giant figure of a woman, taller than their ship. In one hand, raised above her head, she held a torch. The jostling deck grew still. "Liberty" was giving them a welcome.

"What a kindly lady," Pierre whispered.

"Our France gave her to America." His father spoke loudly enough for others to hear. Jean Lefrak had given a few francs to the public fund for the statue when he was still a schoolboy. He had not thought then he'd ever see it, here, in the American harbor. "We gave it to honor the friendship between our peoples. It was the anniversary of their freedom, Pierre. The American Revolution began in 1776—and ours, soon after, in 1789. For more than a hundred years this country has been free!"

Carl looked up at the statue. "There's a poem written by the daughter of an immigrant and sealed in the statue's base," he said. "Recite it, Oscar—in English."

*"Here at our seawashed, sunset gates shall stand*
*A mighty woman with a torch, whose flame*
*Is the imprisoned lightning, and her name*
*Mother of Exiles."*

Oscar   translated—but   translation   was

scarcely needed.   The music of the words carried their own meaning.

Pressed by others around him, Carl turned from the statue to look into their faces.   He saw, reflected in their eyes, the same wonder he felt.   Men stood stiffly, like soldiers at attention.   Pierre's mother, and others, as well, were crying with joy.

The ship passed near the little island on which the statue stood and Oscar continued to recite.   *"Give me your tired, your poor . . . Your huddled masses yearning to breathe free . . . I lift my lamp beside the golden door!"*

\*     \*     \*

As *La Champagne* entered the main harbor, Carl felt her reduce speed.   Then the chugging engines were silenced and the liner stood by, while a pair of tugboats came alongside to guide her into port.

Carl, an inlander, was amazed at the harbor, full of ships with flags of many countries.   And how skillfully the little tugboats maneuvered the slow-moving liner through the crosscurrents and toward the pier!   On shore a band was playing.

"How nice!" Carl thought.   "And to have someone waiting to greet you."   People on dock were waving and calling out to relatives aboard their ship and passengers on the decks above waving scarves and caps and trying to locate friends.

Carl nudged his companion. "You were right, Oscar. I am glad that I came along with you."

As the French liner edged longways against the dock, they followed the rapid teamwork between ship officers and crew with longshoremen on the piers. Brisk calls from bridge to hole and dock; giant coils of rope speeding through the air; and their ship was tightly moored. Gangplanks were lowered from the upper deck and cabin passengers began filing down the runways.

"When do we go ashore?" Pierre was jumping about trying to glimpse his Uncle Victor on the pier.

"We, in the steerage, must wait until the first class passengers have had their baggage checked through customs," Oscar explained.

An hour passed, then another. The last cabin passengers had collected their bags and left the dock.

"Why don't they let us off?" Oscar asked, growing restless.

The Captain sent one of his officers to

explain that the Immigration Office at Castle Garden had closed for the week end. It would take a full day to interview steerage passengers before they could be admitted. This was Saturday and already past noon.

The immigrants crowded around the ship's officer. Surely they had not heard him aright. "We must stay on board till Monday?"

In the confusion, with everyone talking at once, Oscar's angry voice could be heard above the rest. "Twenty minutes from my cousins in Brooklyn and we can't go ashore!"

Carl stood quietly to one side. "Since there is no help for it," he said, "let's make the time pass in a hurry."

Oscar watched him gather Pierre and other children for games. Then getting into the spirit of it, someone began to sing a folksong. Soon circles were formed for dances from the Old Country. "Before we go our many ways," the immigrants said, "we will celebrate together our arrival in America."

That night Carl and Oscar took their pallets on deck, where they could watch the lights of the city.

Sunday, to all held aboard, seemed a day without end. People lined the railing and milled about, staring at the ships and ferry boats. Not even Carl could pretend high spirits.

Before the first light on Monday, he and Oscar carried their small trunks and bundles on deck where anxious families, loaded down with all their possessions, were waiting.

When, at last, immigration officials came aboard, they singled out Oscar and another naturalized citizen, examined their papers and told them, "You may go ashore. Everyone else form in two lines!"

Pierre tugged on Carl's hand. "Your friend will wait for you?"

Carl nodded. The child must guess how alone he felt. If only they had not separated him from Oscar! This was something not foreseen.

A solemn-faced man in uniform passed down the line, stopping to give each immigrant a tag fastened on a cord. He said something in rapid English, and motioned for Carl to hang the tag around his neck.

The line in which the Lefraks stood had been directed to move along the runway to shore. Pierre turned to call again, "Au revoir, Carl!" He broke away from his parents and ran over. "Come to Milwaukee. Remember!"

Carl stood looking down at the small iden-

tification tag on his jacket. "I am no longer
Carl Steinmetz," he thought, "but Number
DX 29583."

As he stood in the examiner's office at Castle
Garden, he struggled against uneasiness.
These two men eyeing him and asking rapid
questions—what must they think of him? A
sorry figure he made: Number DX 29583!

"Do you speak English?" one of the men
asked.

Of the dozen words Carl knew, all deserted
him but one. He clutched at it.

"Do you speak English?" the man asked
again.

"Few."

"Do you have money, or other means to
take care of yourself?"

"Few."

"Do you have relatives to support you?"

"Not relatives. No." He could not say
that Oscar was a relative—though they were
as close as brothers. How could he make
these officials understand him, see beyond his
dwarfed body and clumsy tongue?

"Do you have a trade?" The man sounded
impatient.

Hastily and in German, Carl tried to explain. He was a young scientist come to find

work. He had a friend with whom he would live. He had a letter to a man who owned a factory—another to the engineer at the plant of Thomas Edison. He had dreams of making electricity a mighty power in the people's lives. Just let him prove himself. Let him show how hard and joyously he could work!

Seeing that they did not understand German, Carl tried French, then, the Greek he had learned during his days at the University of Breslau. Surely these men were scholars, learned men entrusted by their government with such a responsible work. Surely they knew Greek?

He saw the immigration officials exchange a meaningful glance and he realized how he must appear to them: shabbily dressed, without the language, without resources or means of support, and badly handicapped.

The officials had stopped their questioning. Carl watched them talking together in whispers. They were coming to some decision about him and their judgment would be final.

At last, one of the immigration officials returned. Although Carl was not able to understand all of the words, their meaning was clear. "There is danger of your becoming a public charge.  We are sorry.  It will be better for you, if you return to your own country."

\*     \*     \*

Oscar cleared his books and baggage through customs.  Then he waited by Castle Garden's exit for Carl, who was not in the first crowd, nor in the next.  None of the immigrants coming out remembered seeing the little hunchback after they landed.  Oscar looked around for a guard to let him go inside to look for his friend.  He had not found one when the Lefraks came through the exit.

Pierre ran over.  "They are sending Carl back!"

"It is true," Pierre's father said.  "They have already taken young Steinmetz to the barbed wire enclosure on another pier.  Those refused entrance must wait there until a place is found on a ship returning to Europe."

Oscar ran up Twelfth Avenue, dodging recklessly among horse teams and heavy drays loaded with ship's cargo.

*"They are sending him back!  Why did you leave him?"*  Little Pierre's words kept running through his head.

Oscar had trouble finding the right pier.

Out of breath, his hand-trunk knocking against his legs, he hurried to the locked gate of the enclosure.

No guard or official was in sight. Behind the barbed wire he saw a handful of people— an old man with a straggly beard—a widow surrounded by her young children. Carl was sitting huddled up on his wooden trunk, looking down at the river.

"Carl!" Oscar set down his own baggage and reached through the fence to take his friend's hand. "We'll have you out of here in no time."

Carl started to make some joke about the tag on his chest, then with a quick glance at his friend's face, said, "The most important examination I ever took, Oscar! And I flunked it. I can see their point—I have no job, no money." He fingered the tag and tried to smile. "Don't think I am giving up. I will learn English and save passage money. Next year I will try again."

"Don't talk nonsense," Oscar said. "You are coming ashore now. Who is in charge here?" He looked around for an official. "This place! They have you penned up here like animals."

Carl shrugged. "It is not very pleasant. Especially for the children."

An immigration official was coming along the wharf. Oscar took out his wallet and, when Carl was not looking, slipped it through the barbed wire into his friend's pocket. Then he walked over to the officer.

Carl could not follow the exchange of heated words. But several times he caught his name and saw the officer glance in his direction.

Finally Oscar brought the man over to the fence. "You will see there has been a serious mistake. My friend is well supplied with funds." He reached into Carl's pocket, pulled out the wallet, and held it up triumphantly.

"But where . . . ?" Carl stared at the roll of bills. Oscar nudged him to be silent.

"We thought him penniless." The officer appeared startled.

"My friend is an engineer and scientist with fine prospects."

"Why didn't he tell us?"

"He did not understand you. Also, he is very modest. But I can tell you about him. He has already made a name for himself in Europe. He has published over twenty articles in scientific magazines." Oscar opened his trunk and pulled out a small schoolbook. "See this book on astronomy? He wrote it."

The officer examined the front pages, making sure of its title and author. The book was in German but the author was unmistakably one *Carl Steinmetz*.

"It is fortunate that I came in time." Oscar was growing bolder. "If you refused admittance to this gifted young man, just imagine the scandal."

"Are we supposed to be mind readers?" The official was looking from this well-dressed American to his shabby companion. It was just possible: yes, sometimes it happened that they made a mistake.

"What if you became known as the man who kept the genius, Carl Steinmetz, out of America?"

"Come now, Mr. Asmussen. It is hardly our fault that he did not know English. We did not understand."

"But now that you do?" Oscar made a slight bow. "I see you will have the good judgment to admit him."

The official hesitated. Genius or no genius, the cripple might become a public charge. "Will you see to him?"

Oscar smiled. "No more than he will see to me. We are together."

The officer went to bring his superior. They returned with Carl's papers. After the proper documents were signed, the officer unlocked the gate. He beckoned Carl outside.

"Come on!" Oscar took him by the arm. "Let's get out of here."

As soon as they were beyond hearing, Carl asked, "How did you manage it?" Chuckling, he handed Oscar his wallet. "This is a new talent of yours, a pickpocket in reverse!"

When they left the wharf and stepped onto the street, Carl put down his bundles.

"What is wrong?" his companion asked.

"I can hardly believe it." Carl was touching the earth beneath his feet. He was on American soil.

## "I Am a Greenhorn"

⫷ WORKING THEIR WAY THROUGH waterfront traffic, past markets and taverns, Oscar pulled his companion by the arm.

"Why is everyone hurrying so?" Carl tried to look into the faces of people who kept shoving their way past them. "Where are they going?" He leaned back for a good look at the buildings. Some of them were ten, even twelve stories high, much higher than in Europe.

"Quit staring," Oscar said. "They'll take you for a greenhorn."

Carl laughed. "I *am* a greenhorn." He

wanted time to study things a bit. So many different people jostling each other—very old and very young, white-skinned and black. Among the crowd he saw only one couple moving with slow dignity. The man had black braids and was wrapped in a blanket. The woman had a small red-skinned baby strapped to her back. Indians! They could have stepped out of a novel by James Fenimore Cooper.

So, Carl thought, even the fairy tales his grandmother told him were true. . . . Here, where everyone was different, he would not feel set apart from the rest. He wished he could talk with his new countrymen. Tomorrow—no, this very night—he would start in earnest learning to speak English.

While Oscar went across a street to buy a newspaper, Carl stood waiting for him and guarding their baggage. A man in a checkered suit and brown derby hat edged up. "You are a newcomer here?" The man spoke hurriedly and in German. "I can help you. Come with me to the Seahawk Tavern, just around the corner." He was already reaching for Carl's steamer trunk. "My buddy is waiting there. He'll give you a fine-paying job."

Carl was wondering at the stranger's kindness, when Oscar returned. "Get along with you!" he said. "We want none of your kind!"

Without a word, the man hurried off.

"Why were you rude to him?" Carl asked. "He only offered to help get me a job."

"A blow on the head and your bags looted, that's what you'd gotten," Oscar said. "These hawks lie in wait for trusting green-horns like you."

On 14th Street they stood in line to board a crosstown horsecar. Carl eyed the pair of horses that must pull the car across Manhattan. They were powerful beasts with thick ankles and heaving sides, but they looked old and worn. "We are too many for the horses to pull," he murmured.

"They are used to it," Oscar shrugged.

All the same, Carl was thinking, it will be much better when we can put power-run motors in their place. He began talking about the new electric motors being tested out here, and also in parts of Europe. He had been studying the principles and designs of these machines. So far they did not work too well. Once they were perfected . . .

"Then the horses can be let out to pasture?" Oscar asked. He liked to tease Carl some-times, for it seemed to him that his friend expected too much of this new power in the world.

At the far end of the line, they left the horsecar and boarded a ferry. Carl stood by the rail looking overhead at the glorious Brooklyn Bridge. What an engineering feat!

"Just see you don't fall for the old gag and let someone sell you stock in it," Oscar cautioned. The bridge, started soon after the Civil War, had taken seventeen years to finish. It had been opened to traffic for six years but the wonder of its great span suspended over the river was still fresh.

A hand organ was grinding "Funiculi Funicula," on the upper deck. Presently the organ-grinder worked his way below deck and a little monkey in a red vest and cap passed a cup. They dropped in coins and Carl leaned down to shake hands with the little fellow, whose bright eyes and wistful face looked almost human.

"Chico, he is name'," the organ grinder said, with a broad smile.

The ferry knocked against the bumpers in the Brooklyn slip and Carl found himself being jostled ashore.

Oscar's cousins lived in a small, coldwater flat just off Atlantic Avenue. The two weary travelers climbed three flights, rested their baggage on the floor, and knocked. The door opened and Carl saw a man even taller than his friend, with the same blond coloring and stubborn jaw.

"Oscar!" With a shout, the man wrapped his arms about his cousin. "Helva!" he called over his shoulder. "Come quick. See who came in off the boat!"

Erik Asmussen turned to Carl. "And you are Oscar's friend? Welcome."

His wife, Helva, gave Carl both hands. "Eight days on the boat!" she said in German. "I remember my own trip over. We were eleven days on the water. You must be tired —and very hungry. Come inside."

Carl soon felt at home with Oscar's cousins. He gave them an amusing account of the way Oscar had rescued him from the immigration officials at Castle Garden and made his friend repeat his trick with the wallet.

"Oscar, what was it you told the official to make his face so red?" Carl asked.

"You'd better not ask." Turning to his cousins, Oscar explained that he had declared that young Steinmetz was a genius who would do big things for America.

Carl looked uncomfortable. "Wouldn't you

say, to put it mildly, you exaggerated?" he asked.

"Perhaps I did—a little. But the funny thing is, I believe it."

"You will find that you sometimes have to bluff a little, to impress people," Erik said. "Maybe they expect it. It is what we call 'Toot your own horn!'"

"But Oscar never blows for himself." Carl answered in a troubled voice. "Only for me."

"And if he hadn't, where would you be now? On the high seas," Helva said gently.

"Maybe you can't brag, Carl, but it is beyond me"—Oscar looked at his friend— "You had your letter of introduction to the engineer at the Edison plant. And the other one to the man in Yonkers. Why didn't you show them to the immigration official?"

Carl shrugged. "They are only letters, not a job."

Helva refilled their coffee cups and brought out a Danish cheese she kept hidden away for a holiday treat.

"It's a celebration!" Carl said and the two boys laughed at a secret shared.

Erik turned to his cousin. "And what of your plans? You must stay here with us, both of you, before you start on to California."

"I am not going to California." Oscar told

about his break with their uncle and about the girl he meant to marry.

"You are right, Oscar. There are more things in life than making money." Helva's blue eyes sparkled as she asked about Louisa and studied the picture Oscar took from his wallet.

"She has a good face. Yes, I think I shall like her. Just imagine, Erik, Oscar is staying on here, and we're getting a new cousin."

Erik nodded. That part was good, but Oscar better think his decision over carefully. "Perhaps you ought to make it up with Uncle Josef? Someday you would be the head of his whole business. You are throwing away a sure future," Erik said.

"Expand—expand! That's all Uncle Josef knows. For what? Carl, here, knows I am right."

"Surely everybody wants to get ahead," Erik insisted.

When Oscar did not answer, Carl asked, "Just what is this 'get ahead'? Ahead of what? Ahead of other people?"

"Of course not. Just ahead! Make a success. That's America."

"Oscar wants to make a success," Carl said. "It is just that he does not agree with his uncle's idea of a successful life. There is room in this great country for many kinds of success. Is that not so?"

Helva nodded vigorously. Then she jumped up with a laugh. "There is room. But in our apartment you must set the kitchen table in corner before we can unfold the cots which you will sleep on. Come, it's time for bed!"

"Wait," Erik said. "We must be practical. If Oscar and Carl want jobs in New York, they must look in the newspaper in the Help Wanted column."

"But Carl has a letter to the Edison electric light plant!" Oscar said.

"We will try there, for both of us," Carl replied quickly.

"No," Oscar studied the newspaper. "You are the electrical genius. The Edison plant would not be for me. A plain job, a place to live and the money to send for Louisa!" He began reading the list of openings and marking them down.

"You are both welcome to stay with us until you get settled if you don't mind being crowded," Erik said as he set up the cots and set the alarm clock for 5 o'clock.

Oscar protested. "Why so early?"

"Even at 6:00," Erik told him, "you will find others ahead of you."

Carl stood by the kitchen window looking out on the tall dark buildings huddled together. He could hear shrill voices: laughter, quarreling, a snatch of song in the language he could not understand. He was really in America, three thousand miles away from his father . . . He looked overhead at Orion and Jupiter. The stars at least were the same as in Europe. Tomorrow he would find work and begin a new life.

\* \* \*

"You're sure there is no use going back to Edison's?" It was dark and the two friends had met on the ferry crossing from Manhattan to Brooklyn. A wet fog drifted in from the ocean almost blotting out the lights of the shorefront and turning the electric lights on the big bridge into pale yellow balls. The muffled warning of bell buoys guided the crowded ferry to the unseen Brooklyn pier.

"I am sure," Carl answered. "The engineer was quite firm about it. My letter seemed to upset him. 'What do you expect of us,' he said, 'to find everybody jobs? Is everybody in Europe who knows a little about electricity going to come here, expecting to work with Mr. Edison?' I think he did not like foreigners to come."

Oscar knew that Carl had counted on working at the electric light plant. On the trip over he had heard little else than Edison and his pioneering. But Carl had still another letter, to Mr. Eickemeyer in Yonkers. "Tomorrow you must take the train to Yonkers," he said.

"And you?" Carl asked. "How did you make out?"

Oscar leaned back on the bench and thrust out his aching feet. "I used up a lot of shoe leather but that is all."

Helva had been watching for them. She remembered what it had been like, a new-comer job hunting in the big city. Oscar would manage, but she felt troubled about Carl.

"You boys!" She drew them inside. "I bet you have eaten nothing all day. Don't I know! When I first came, was I a greenhorn! I did not know English, not even how to read street signs. I wore my shoes thin, looking for work. When I came home, I used to soak my tired feet and have a good cry. Next day I would start out again."

"And then," Oscar said, "you met Erik."

"No, silly. Much later. I found a place making overalls: a dark loft crowded with sewing machines and girls from Italy and Poland, greenhorns like myself. In the trade we call it a sweat shop. Most of us worked right through lunch; peddling away on our machines, with a sandwich in one hand. We'd call back and forth the few words we had picked up in English. *Pay day. How much? Boss.*"

"English," Carl shook his head. "It is so important to learn the language. I could not even talk to little children playing in the street."

He reached in his pocket and pulled out a little notebook. "I could not talk, but I listened. Look I have a list of twenty words already!"

Helva peered over his shoulder, puzzled. There were no words just little marks on the page.

"That's Carl's shorthand," Oscar said. "He invented it himself and he can write as fast as he thinks. In school he could take down every word of the professors' lectures and read them back to us. It's like magic."

"It's a good magic," Helva said approvingly and all through supper she gave Carl new words for his list. She held up a slice of bread, a knife, a cup, and watched Carl write the words down. She pointed to a chair, to the table, the clock, naming each object.

After the dishes were over she pushed her chair back and sat erect with a lordly manner. "I am the plant manager at Yonkers. Come, Carl, ask me for a job, now. And mind you, not a word of German!"

Carl did not know how to begin. He looked around helplessly for Oscar. But Oscar was busy with the evening paper.

Carl consulted his note book. "Good morning, sir. Have I the honor Mr. Rudolph Eickemeyer to speak with?"

Oscar looked up from the Help Wanted column. "Here's a Manhattan tooling plant that's hiring mechanics and draftsmen," he said to Erik in a low voice, so as not to interrupt Helva's game.

"We'll set the alarm for 4:30," Erik answered. "With luck on the ferry, you'll make it there by 6:00."

Oscar groaned. "4:30? That's the dead of night!"

But before dawn next morning Carl and Oscar were running the last blocks to the ferry. Even at that early hour, the docks were crowded with workmen crossing the river to their jobs. The horsecars which took the two boys uptown were even more jammed.

Carl made sure he had the letter to Mr. Eickemeyer in his pockets. He had Oscar repeat the directions for getting to Yonkers, then wrote out a few questions he might need in finding his way.

"You leave the car at 125th Street," Oscar said. "To Yonkers, by train will take you two hours."

When the horsecar stopped at 125th Street, Carl pushed his way to the street.

"Remember," Oscar called, "turn east for the station. Good luck!" and Carl was alone.

\* \* \*

People and traffic, even the buildings seemed to be pressing in on him. He looked overhead, taking his direction from the sun, then walked the long blocks east. It was a little frightening to know he could not talk to anyone.

In the railroad station he watched to see where people were going for tickets, then pulled out the money Oscar had loaned him and in a firm voice said, "Yonkers, please."

Surprised that he had managed this so easily, he followed others to an upstairs platform.  By the sun, the train was traveling north, as it should.  After many stops the conductor would call out, "Yonkers!" and he would be facing Mr. Eickemeyer.  He recalled what Mr. Uppenborn, the editor in Zurick, had told him about this man.  "Your standing up to Bismarck will be in your favor. Rudolph Eickemeyer did the same in his time. In fact, you may find much in common.  He is an inventor in his own right."

Carl went over the letter in his mind.  Mr. Uppenborn had spoken very kindly of his article about the new machines called electrical transformers.  "But I must not count too heavily on this," Carl said to himself.

The train moved jerkily around a curve and entered a low roadbed along the river, and Carl saw, for the first time, the full sweep of the Hudson.  How swift and deep she ran, this American river!  On the far bank rose shining cliffs.  "This river and these cliffs and bright sky," Carl thought, "they are mine, too.  This is my country.  I will find my place here."

As he left the train in Yonkers he noticed a sign in tall letters on a brick wall of a building: *Eickemeyer and Osterholt*.  Without giving himself time to worry about what he was going to say, he limped down the station stairs and made his way to the factory entrance.

A young man with smooth hands and a cool manner sat behind a desk near the door. Taking off his hat, Carl bowed. "Good morning, sir. Please, Herr Eickemeyer."

He felt the young man bore through him with unfriendly eyes. Carl thought: it is always the same—first they see the hump on my back, before they see me. . . .

"You wish to see Mr. Eickemeyer?"

Carl nodded. "Please, for Mr. Eickemeyer I have the letter."

The young man frowned, smoothed his hair, and disappeared up a stairway.

After a moment he heard a heavy tread on the stairs and a large man strode toward him. He had a flowing, iron-gray beard that reached to his chest, and the bearing of a man used to handling important affairs.

Carl put his heels together, as students in Europe were taught to do and bowed. "Have me the honor Herr Eickemeyer to speak with?"

The big man looked steadily at him for a moment, then held out his hand. "Let us speak German," he said and motioned Carl to a chair. With relief, Carl brought out the letter of introduction and waited quietly while Rudolph Eickemeyer read it.

"Hans Uppenborn writes that he has published an article by you on the new electric transformer." Mr. Eickemeyer glanced up and his eyes were bright with interest. "We have been having some trouble with transformers. Have they found any way in Europe to prevent the motors from overheating and soon burning out?"

Carl talked eagerly. It was not hard to ask at the end of the conversation, "Would you have a place for me?"

Mr. Eickemeyer appeared to be thinking it over. "Not at this time. I am sorry. As a matter of fact we do almost no electrical work here. In the future, perhaps. Our shop at present is taken up repairing machines for making hats. Hardly your line."

Carl said, "I am willing to do anything."

Rudolph Eickemeyer stood up and held out his hand. "I have enjoyed our talk. If some opening comes up, we will let you know."

*      *      *

The train back to New York was a long time in coming. When Carl reached Brooklyn, workmen were already leaving the factories and flooding the streets. Work, Carl thought. All these people have work. When you have work, you take it for granted, when you don't, the world seems empty. You don't belong.

A woman, bent with age and carrying a basket of flowers on her arm, came up to him. "Buy my flowers. Please buy." She held out violets, then a bunch of lilies of the valley.

Carl consulted his notebook. "How much?" he asked carefully. Every May when he was younger he had picked the sweet-smelling, white bells in Germany. He counted the coins left in his pocket, glad now that he'd had no appetite for eating at noon-time. He was sure that Helva Asmussen would like May flowers. When she opened the door he held out the lilies.

"But how beautiful! Look, Erik, how they brighten the whole room." She glanced searchingly at Carl. Were the flowers meant as a celebration? Had he found a job?

"If an opening comes up, Herr Eickemeyer will let me know." Carl answered the unspoken question. "Meanwhile . . ." He turned his empty pocket out.

Helva's eyes filled. "Meanwhile you spend your lunch money to buy me flowers."

Oscar came in while they were eating. "Everywhere I go it is the same." He flung his cap on to a chair. "What experience do you have? But—if nobody gives me work, how am I supposed to get experience?" He looked at Erik, eating in silence. "Go ahead, say it! I know what you are thinking."

Erik quietly finished his tea. "You bring up Uncle Josef, not I. But is true, isn't it? Working for him, you would get your experience."

Oscar flushed. "At what price?" He fingered the letter that had just come from Louisa.

"Why not be practical? Uncle Josef could take you both on. Carl meanwhile could be learning English. Then, if you still wanted, before Louisa comes you could leave and take work elsewhere."

"Enough!" Helva said. "If Oscar doesn't want it . . . Carl, what new words did you learn today?"

Carl took out his notebook and they laughed over some words he had learned: *Step lively. Don't push. Dumb foreigner.* Then they did not laugh. From the man sitting behind him in the train, he had learned the word: *hunchback.* Perhaps America was only a land for giants.

\*        \*        \*

Each morning Oscar and Carl started out at five and returned after dark. Each evening they read the Help Wanted column. Their funds were running low. Erik and Helva would not hear of them moving elsewhere, but they knew they must soon find a place of their own.

When their cots were set up and the lights were out, Carl turned on his narrow bed, thinking. When you did not have work, the earth no longer seemed to move. He remembered his father's words. *"Believe in yourself, Carl. The world has need of you. What you are, not how you may appear to other men, is what counts."*

Two weeks passed in this way; then, one evening, Oscar came home, and tossed his cap in the air.

"I have been taken on in a tinware plant!" He waltzed Helva about the room. "It's just making drawings for lunch pails, milk pails, garbage pails—but that doesn't matter!"

"You have found work!" Carl stirred up cheese pancakes, to celebrate, in Zurich fashion. "In good time, so will I."

Tomorrow he would make another trip up to Yonkers. Mr. Eickemeyer had said come again. By this time Mr. Eickemeyer might have an opening.

# On the Track of Something Big

⊂₽ WHEN HE ENTERED THE YONKERS plant, the clerk stared from behind the desk. "You were here before," he said accusingly.

"Yes. Please. Mr. Eickemeyer."

"But he told you, didn't he? There is no opening."

"Yes. Please. Mr. Eickemeyer."

The manager was busy in the plant, the clerk answered. Carl waited until the noon hour. When Rudolph Eickemeyer came through the lobby he looked rather surprised to see Carl. "You have not found work?

Well then, let us come straight to the point. Do you think you could do drafting?"

"Let me try."

"It may not be just what you would prefer?" Mr. Eickemeyer was regarding him closely.

"I would like to try it." In writing his astronomy textbook Carl had done considerable drawing and number work. He had not done much otherwise, outside of the usual college courses. "I take it this will be blueprints for hat-making machines?" he said.

Rudolph Eickemeyer ran his fingers through his beard. "As a matter of fact, no. We have begun developing a new type of electric motor. We will set you to work on these. Come in, on Monday," he said. "We will begin."

Looking down on the river while he waited for his train, Carl was sure the Hudson had never had such a glow. Now I belong, he thought. I have work. America is also for me!

He stood at the rail of the ferryboat watching the lights of Brooklyn Bridge go on. Tonight, at last, he could write his father. And tomorrow not having to trudge the streets looking for work he could explore the city—

for pleasure. Maybe he'd walk the span of the bridge across the river. . . .

When Helva opened the door, Oscar and Erik looked up from the table. Carl stood for a moment smiling at them.

"You got it!" Oscar ran over to shake his hand, then Helva and Erik.

Carl grinned. "Tonight, Oscar, it is your turn to make the pancakes."

\*        \*        \*

"Four flights up and to the rear." The landlord shifted his glance from Oscar to his companion, wondering if these two would prove more likely tenants than the last. To judge by the tall one in the fine suit, they would be on time with the rent. But the hunchback was shabby, except for a gold watch chain across his vest.

"Eight dollars a month it is. In advance," he said, as he unlocked the door on a narrow room that gave out a stale odor of fish and onions.

Carl opened a window. "If you lean out, you can see the Hudson."

Oscar was examining the sagging cots. They had been climbing stairs since early morning, looking for a room to set up housekeeping.

"Shall we take it?" Carl asked doubtfully.

It was no better than a hole in the wall, Oscar grumbled. However, it was near the Yonkers train for Carl and just a half-hour on the horsecars from his own work. Here, at least, they could be together. Yes, he said, they'd better take it.

"Everything is working out as we planned," Carl said, as the two householders dumped the last of their baggage inside the door that evening. "We have jobs and a room together in New York!"

He placed his small, red trunk by his cot and opened the windows to let in the good June air. "It is like old times, Oscar. Instead of the Alps, the Palisades. And for good measure, the Hudson."

His roommate was eyeing the bumps in his mattress. "As soon as we can find a better place, we'll move. This is a dump. It's awful. But I suppose it's all we can afford."

But Carl refused to be discouraged. Watching him move about, talkative and cheerful as the pigeons on the ledge outside, Oscar remembered that in their ten months together he had never known Carl to be low in spirits. "How do you manage it?" he asked.

"Maybe I caught the trick from my grand-mother," Carl answered. "She was Polish. Her people were weavers by trade. From early childhood she knew what it was to sing, work hard and do without. Granny loved people. She never had a chance at schooling, but she had more wisdom than many well-schooled folk."

He reached into his trunk and took out her picture and set it on the worktable. "Look at her," he said. "The face is lined and worn and under the ruffled cap her hair is white, but the eyes! There, you see true happiness. I look often at her picture and I know that life is good."

\*    \*    \*

When Carl reached the Yonkers plant on Monday morning he greeted the clerk in his best English and walked quickly upstairs and into the drafting room.

A slight man carrying a sheaf of blueprints came over to him. "You are my new helper? Mr. Eickemeyer told me to expect you." He peered at Carl over his glasses. "I am Edward Mueller, senior draftsman in charge here."

He led the way over to a drawing board and, speaking in German, explained the work laid out. The precise manner of the European-trained craftsman put Carl at ease. These sheets held separate drawings, Mueller said, for each part of the new motor which Mr. Eickemeyer had designed. "You know about this?"

"Yes, yes. He spoke with me." Carl was anxious to get started.

Edward Mueller was not to be hurried. Young Steinmetz was to check over the drawings, and bring them all to scale. Later he would combine them in a master drawing of the complete motor and all its parts. "Do you think you can do this?"

"I believe so. With your help."

Edward Mueller watched him for awhile then went about his own work. Carl opened his new Work Record Book and made the first entry: *June 10, 1889: started work on street-car motor #3.*

As he studied the drawings he saw that Rudolph Eickemeyer was on the track of something big. There had been many efforts to build a motor that could drive streetcars but none had passed the strain of pulling the load while in motion. Mr. Eickemeyer himself had built two motors that worked on the first test and then failed. This third try was of a different design. To Carl, it looked good.

When Rudolph Eickemeyer came into the drafting room he stood behind Carl's desk watching him at work. Carl was so intent on his drawing and calculations that he was not aware of being watched.

Eickemeyer noticed a strange thing: young Steinmetz was working without his slide rule. No draftsman worked without this tool at his elbow. With a slide rule a person could multiply and divide large numbers with ease and accuracy. It saved much paperwork.

"Where is your slide rule?" Mr. Eickemeyer asked abruptly.

Carl looked up and blushed. He felt a little hesitant about explaining. "I find it easier to work problems in my head. It is a habit I have fallen into. I find that I can work faster this way."

The older man frowned. This young immigrant did not strike him as a braggart, yet it was hard to believe that anyone could do these complex calculations in his head. And as for being faster than a slide rule, that could not be true!

"In drafting work," Mr. Eickemeyer said patiently, "the main thing is accuracy. Each measurement has to be exact. Take the drawings on which you are working. A blueprint

for a motor or machine is similar to a pattern
for a coat. The motor's various parts will be
cut to size, just as a coat is cut from a pattern.
One mistake in figuring would cost days of
wasted labor and material."

"I think you can rely on my accuracy," Carl
said quietly.

"Come now, we will test you out."
Rudolph Eickemeyer took the slide rule and
stated a complicated problem in multiplication.
Carl's answer was prompt and correct.
Eickemeyer tried him on several others, then
switched to ones in division. Right again!
This was a thing you had to see to believe it:
a man faster than a slide rule and as accurate.

"I had thought to take on a draftsman."
Eickemeyer's frown had disappeared. "This
means you are in the first place a mathematician."

"I have always liked figuring." Carl said.
"It comes easily to me. But if you prefer, I
can use the slide rule?"

The older man shrugged. "Do it your way.
But remember, we cannot afford a single
error. We are having trouble enough with
this motor."

Carl bent over his drafting board. When
the workroom emptied for the noon hour

Edward Mueller went over to him. "Time for lunch." Carl wondered where the morning had gone.

Late in the afternoon Rudolph Eickemeyer returned to see how the work was coming along. He checked carefully. Everything was in order.

"I am very happy you have trusted me with this work," Carl said.

"You are no more pleased than I am," the inventor answered. "As you see," he said, "this is model #3. Earlier models, which Stephens Fields and I worked on, have overheated and broken down. From what we can learn other engineers are having the same trouble."

"So I have read," Carl said. "Are you on the track of it?"

"Not yet. The motor heats up—burns itself out. So we try out a new model, test it to find how it stands up—then try again."

*There must be an answer,* Carl thought. On the long trip home he kept thinking about it.

When he got to the room, Oscar was trying to cook hamburgers on the hot, balky stove. "The cranky thing refuses to burn!" He rattled the stove damper.

"Come, leave off. We will eat them as they are," Carl said cheerfully. "On payday we will buy a second-hand gasplate. No more woodfires until winter. After supper we will make out a budget. This place is not perfect but it is cheap. What we save will bring Louisa closer."

The budget-making did not take long. From their combined salaries of twenty-four dollars a week, they decided that they could save five dollars. This amount, Carl insisted, belonged to Oscar. "Even at this rate—" Oscar sighed. "It will be late spring before Louisa and I can be married."

Carl agreed this was a long time to wait. "Perhaps we will get raises. And overtime work. Then we can save faster."

"Perhaps —" Oscar did not finish his thought. Three thousand miles and across the ocean was a long way to expect a lone girl to travel from her family and country.

"Oscar, we have company." Carl pointed under the table. A mouse was running about nibbling up crumbs. "Our first guest. Let's make him welcome." Carl dropped a square of cheese on the floor.

"Start feeding him and in no time we'll be swamped." Oscar reached over to put the cheese away. "This fine fellow has relatives."

Carl dropped a piece of hamburger. "Wherever did he come from?"

"The city has thousands of them. Rats, too." Oscar shuffled his feet and the mouse darted across the floor and disappeared.

But next morning Carl saw their guest had returned, bringing with him a companion. "Brave fellows!" he chuckled. "I will name you Pied and Piper, though Harlem is not a fairy tale spot like Hamelin." With Oscar asleep, he could feed them as many tidbits as he liked.

At suppertime Pied and Piper appeared again. Oscar, happy over a letter from Louisa, dropped them a slice of raisin bread. "They do make good company."

Carl pointed to the full sink. "Whose turn to do the dishes?"

"Yours."

"But I did them yesterday."

"Well then, let's stack them," Oscar said. Efficiency was a key word with engineers and it was clearly wasteful to wash a few dishes twice a day, fourteen times a week. They would wait till all dishes had been used up, then make a quick job of it and start over.

Laughing, Carl agreed. He took down the

dictionary and began puzzling out words in the New York paper. He liked the American language. It was like the people, full of vigor.

In the morning he jostled Oscar's cot. "This efficiency get-out-of-work scheme of yours! There's a hitch in it."

"Did you wake me for that!"

"But how can I make eggs for breakfast? No frying pan." He hunted under the pile of dishes for the skillet. "After this, Oscar. No clean frying pan—no eggs."

Carl was pleased over one thing: Pied and Piper had brought along a companion. He began to look forward to their visits, especially in the early morning when he wanted someone to keep him company. Oscar was useless until he had breakfast inside him.

A few weeks later, Oscar was counting their small guests underfoot. Every night there were more.

"They are growing quite friendly," Carl said.

"Too friendly. They must be making a nest somewhere about." Oscar looked inside the iron stove they had abandoned. On top of a pile of papers stuffed in the oven, the mice had set up housekeeping.

"Carl, they are getting out of hand. We

had better call a halt before they take over
the place."

"These wee things?" Carl was on his
knees, coaxing a mouse to take cheese off his
finger. "Come, Piper!" His pet had been
caught in a neighbor's trap and had a game
leg. "Piper is a bright one. I shall teach him
tricks."

Out of a wooden box the grocer gave him,
Carl built a maze, a series of interlocking
alleyways. When Piper or Pied found their
way through the crooked paths a prize was
waiting: a piece of cheese. Piper soon knew
his way about but Pied grew confused in the
maze. The little mouse looked so downcast
that Carl often helped him out.

It was a time of warm happiness to Carl—
at home and at work, he was content that
summer. In August a note came from Helva
Asmussen announcing the birth of a baby girl.
"Come over to Brooklyn Sunday," she wrote.
"*I* will make the pancakes."

They journeyed by horsecar to the ferry,
carrying toys and a doll. One of the work
horses fell in the street, overcome by the heat.

"The load is too heavy," Carl mourned. If
only Eickemeyer's motor worked! Electric
power must be made to take over burdens too

heavy for living things. He had a thought about the blueprint on his desk and took out his notebook to jot some figures down.

Oscar did not share Carl's faith in this new force. "Six days a week you eat and sleep electric motors. Must we have them on a holiday Sunday as well?"

"When I leave the plant, do you expect me to stop thinking? There is so much to find out, Oscar. So much we don't know."

"How much good will come of it?"

"No one can foresee the end of it. Electric power will remake the world." Carl had finished his notes. "Much heavy labor now done by animals and man can be saved: lifting, loading, pulling. Men harvesting crops; women bent over washtubs and floors, scrubbing, scrubbing. In time we will have machines to do all these things."

"Now, who is dreaming? You're asking for miracles."

"It will come," Carl said.

At the Atlantic Avenue apartment, Helva led them to the baby's cradle. Isn't she beautiful?" she whispered. "Look at her hands."

Carl reached down and touched one tiny fist with his finger. Nature created many things that to men seemed miracles. None equaled this. "Yes, Helva, she is beautiful."

When they returned to their room in Harlem they found the mice up on the shelves raiding their food supplies.

"Carl, they are over-running the place. We must set traps."

"But these are our friends! It is quite simple; we must put our food in cans and covered tins."

Evenings, when Carl sat up late making notes from a new German book on terrestrial magnetism and electricity, Piper nibbled at his shoelaces. He didn't mind this, but when his pets began to feed on his papers and books he knew that Oscar was right: the situation was getting out of hand. Furthermore, October was not far off—they'd have to start a fire in the stove these small guests had taken for their home.

Something would have to be done.

On the day that Carl came home to find Oscar cooking supper in his overcoat, it was clear the question couldn't be put off any longer.

"We are going to have to start the stove," Carl said.

"Yes, I know. What are we going to do about the mice?"

Carl was silent. Must they set traps for friends?

"It has come to the place," Oscar persisted. "It's them or us."

"Watch your grammar," Carl said with a smile. In these few months his English had improved greatly.

"Bother the grammar. My meaning is clear. Either they leave or we do."

"We need a better place anyhow," his roommate said. "And we can afford to spend a little more now that Mr. Eickemeyer has raised your salary."

"Right. I can have a corner for a lab."

"No, you don't! We had enough of that in Zurich."

When they moved to their new room, a few blocks away, Oscar searched his friend's pockets, to make sure Carl was not carrying Pied and Piper along.

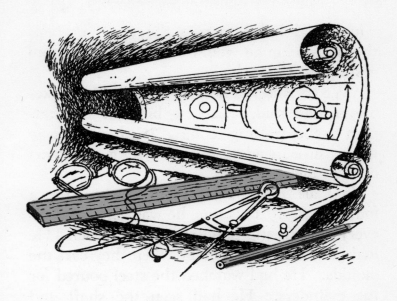

# The Tryout

⊏⊐ THE FIRST DAYS OF SPRING
brought special joys. German bands appeared
nightly in the courtyard of their new home
and the air was filled with brassy but old,
familiar tunes. The dawns were green and
gold for Carl's daily rides along the banks of
the Hudson. Money had been saved for
Louisa Bergson's passage. In another month
she would be on the water, heading for America.

And, at the plant, Carl had finished the
blueprints for motor #4! The design was
only slightly different from motor #3,

which had failed to pass the test. Perhaps the slight change would keep the motor from getting overheated. . . .

"We try and fail and try again," Mr. Eicke-meyer had said, when he brought the new plan to the drafting room. "We have no way to measure in advance how strong each part of the motor must be."

So Carl had made the blueprints for a fourth motor. This time he was able to follow every step in the building of the model. He had gone into the foundry when they cast the moulds. He had watched the steel poured for the cylinders. He had seen the shaft and other parts, for which he had drawn blue-prints, take shape and become real.

He spent hours in the machine shop watch-ing the skilled craftsmen tool the fine parts and begin assembling. Tom Wercke, the chief mechanic, and Will, his helper, became used to having Carl around. They even let him lend a hand winding copper wires around the motor's soft magnetic center. "The arma-ture," they called this inner part through which the electric current would pass.

*Armature*, Carl repeated the word several times. That night it went into his notebook. Hundreds of English words were now on his list, written in that shorthand Helva Asmussen still called magic. He practiced the words aloud until he could say them without stumbling.

When the armature was set into its frame and connected to the shaft that would drive the wheels, motor #4 was ready for testing.

Next morning Carl set his alarm clock for 4:30 and traveled to Yonkers. But when he came to the shop Mr. Eickemeyer and Tom Wercke were there before him. The noisy motor vibrated through the shop—a beautiful sound!

"Is she holding up?" Carl asked.

The inventor gave him a brisk nod. "You are early, young man."

Switching off the current, Mr. Eickemeyer began a thorough check of the model. Beneath his quiet manner Carl sensed keen excitement.

His own heart was pounding when the gray-bearded man straightened up and said, "I think she is ready for a tryout on a streetcar. Would you like to come along? We have the tryouts on Steinway Road in Brooklyn—Yonkers has no suitable streetcar tracks with a power plant nearby. And we make the tests on Sundays. On Sunday afternoons, the Brooklyn line can be cleared for our use."

It was a long haul from Yonkers to the Brooklyn carbarn. A huge dray carried several models of the new motor and also the overhead trolley. The two mechanics made room for Carl between them on the driver's seat. A couple of other men from the shop sat with legs outstretched between the machines.

The boss, they said, and his partner, Mr. Stephen Fields, had gone down the night before. Mr. Eickemeyer wanted to make sure that the poles and overhead wires were in place and to arrange for electric power.

"You'll see how everybody turns out," Tom Wercke chuckled. "You'd think Barnum's circus had come to Brooklyn, or a troop of dancing bears! They crowd around until we have to clear the tracks before we can get started."

Tom and Will filled the time of the journey with stories of earlier tryouts of horsecars run without horses.

"When the first car started off you'd 'a' thought the end of the world had come," Tom said. "When the motor started smoking and broke down, the crowd gave us the horse-laugh. Same with motor #2, though it got a little farther across town."

"And #3 never made the grade as far as Brooklyn, worse luck," Tom said.

"Do you think the new motor will go?" Carl asked anxiously.

"I wouldn't put any odds on the old girl," Tom answered. "We've got four machines, all just alike. If one acts up, we can replace it with others. But you never can tell."

"Mr. Eickemeyer sets a store by these motors," Will said. "I sure hope they work."

"If not these, then others," Carl said. "But 'try and fail and try again'—that is a slow method."

The team had come the length of Manhattan, to the entrance of the Brooklyn Bridge. The drive across the glorious span was made at a quick pace. Carl would have been content to have it last longer if he had not been so anxious for the tryout to begin. "The great bridge," he said, "that, too, took many years!"

As they started up the main avenue from Fulton Street he noticed a gang of boys pointing to the trolley dangling from the back of the dray. "It's that horseless streetcar again!" they chanted and fell in behind at a trot. "Free circus! See the electric streetcar!"

By the time the dray reached Steinway Road a crowd was following along, hooting and calling good-naturedly, in holiday spirit. "Free rides!  Come risk your neck in the horseless streetcar."

"If she covers five blocks before she breaks down, I'll stand treats."

Waiting in the carbarn was the wooden streetcar, painted an ugly yellow.  The horses had been unharnessed and were eating from feedbags hung about their necks.

Rudolph Eickemeyer had completed his inspection of the car tracks and overhead cable.  He came into the carbarn to see to installing the motors and rigging up the overhead trolley.  Under his wide-brimmed black hat his face looked pale and a little drawn; but his eyes glowed.  In his high-buttoned coat, he could have been taken for a scholar, or a preacher rather than a successful engineer.

"Everything ready?"

"Ready!"

With a grave nod, the dignified inventor took his place at the controls.  Behind him sat Stephen Fields.  Carl climbed aboard with Tom and Will.  The cry went out to clear the tracks and the crowd backed slowly away.

As Rudolph Eickemeyer threw on the

power, Carl leaned forward as if to give the car a push ahead. With a rough jerk, the horseless car left the barn and switched onto the main track.

A gasp ran through the crowd of by-standers. They were seeing the impossible. This car without horses was moving. Some ran for cover. A workman threw his cap in the air. "Hurrah!" he shouted. "Keep going!"

"Are my old eyes deceiving me?" a man muttered. "It's a miracle that's what it is." To think he had left Ireland to witness such doings! There was nothing like this in the Old Country.

The motor roared. A flash, bright as light-ning, ran along the wheels and an old woman crossed herself. "It's dark magic. Playing with forces of evil."

"It's magic, Aunty," the workman an-swered," but I'm doubting if there's anything that's evil in it. It's the new age."

A miracle, yes, another said, a miracle worked by science.

Others disagreed in loud voices.

"This new-fangled thing, electricity. I don't trust it. What's wrong with horses?"

"You mean we should creep along at eight

miles an hour when we could go all of fifteen —maybe twenty!"

"My! What's to keep us all from getting killed? Electrocuted!"

"Whatever's that?"

"That's what they call it. You get killed by current, same as struck down by lightning. A body goes all purple."

Mr. Eickemeyer brought the car to a stop and leaned out. "We have room for six more passengers," he said.

Some held back, but others, more daring, scrambled aboard. As the car picked up speed, bystanders trotted alongside trying to keep up, pointing and joking and waiting for the horseless thing to break down. Soon the car was moving faster than horses ever had been able to travel, even when pulling at their best. New crowds ran alongside when the others had been left behind. Rudolph Eickemeyer, his beard lifting in the breeze, stood with shoulders erect, eyes straight ahead, a captain piloting his craft through tricky waters.

Abruptly, the trolley slipped off the overhead wire with a crack and a sputter. The crowd fell back while Will climbed out and set it right. Then, one motor burned out.

There was a halt while the second was connected to the current. That one became overheated, too. The third and fourth were tried. After a short distance they broke down dismally.

The crowd following the car was jeering openly, now. "Old Miracle Worker has died on us."

"Haul Old Miracle back to the barn."

"Yeah—and hitch up Dobbin. Slow but sure."

"Right! I want to be certain of getting to the job tomorrow."

Horses had to be hitched to the streetcar to haul it back to the barn.

Silently Tom and Will and the other mechanics went back to load the dead motors into the dray. Carl walked to the carshed with Mr. Eickemeyer, who looked suddenly old and tired. But he said, "Next Sunday we will try again."

One of the bystanders overheard the promise and laughed. "Don't you inventors know when to say quits?"

Carl did not return to Yonkers. He saw that he was near Atlantic Avenue and stopped off at the Asmussens to tell them about the failure. "They are not giving up," he explained. "Next week we'll have another tryout."

Helva said, "Erik, we'll go aboard."

"Perhaps. But what about the baby? Don't you think she is a little young yet?"

"Let her miss an adventure like this? Some day she will tell 'her grandchildren about it. 'I rode with Carl Steinmetz in the first horse-less cars in Brooklyn!' "

Carl's smile was rueful. "It may prove a short ride."

The machine shop was a busy place all week making changes in the motors and building a brace Mr. Fields had designed to keep the trolley in place.

On the next Sunday, the crowd gathered early to watch, and perhaps even to venture a ride on the electric-run trolley.

Carl saw the Asmussens waiting near the carbarn and hurried to help them aboard. As Helva went up the steps, holding the baby, a woman pulled her sleeve. "How can you take that little innocent?"

"Why should she be afraid?" Helva answered. "Look she is smiling!"

Things went well at first, but half-way across town the trolley lines broke. Over-weighted by the new magnetized switch, the trolley crashed to the ground, barely missing the roof of the car.

Passengers left the car and refused to board it again. If the wires had landed on the car, they said, we might all have been killed. Electrocuted! Even Helva lost her courage.

"*Now* will you call it quits?" someone shouted to Rudolph Eickemeyer as horses arrived to pull the car back to the barn.

The inventor walked off, without answering.

"Do you think we will?" Tom Wercke asked.

"Quit?" Carl was surprised. "We have only started."

\*    \*    \*

The next day Carl asked for time off and hurried down to the Naturalization Office to take out his first papers to become a citizen of the United States. That evening he raced up the stairs to their room. "Oscar!" he called, "I passed! I made it."

Out of breath, he dropped on to his cot, holding out the papers to his roommate. "Think of it, Oscar! In five years I will be a full citizen."

Oscar looked over the papers. "Isn't this

a mistake? You have signed your name Charles—not Carl."

"That is how it is going to be. I am an American. Carl, in English, is Charles. Right? In my speech, my name, everything I shall be one with this country. *Charles P. Steinmetz.* Do you know in the shop in the morning, they say not just 'good morning' but 'Hey! What's new!' And at night it is not 'good-by' but 'So long, Charlie.' This American slang—I like it."

"And the *P?* What's that for?" Oscar persisted.

Charles laughed. "I just thought up the middle initial. It's for Proteus. Do you remember I told you that the students in Breslau University used to call me Proteus? For the Greek sea god who could take such curious shapes. At first, when they called me that, I thought it was because of the hump on my back. I thought they were making fun of my deformity."

"You should have known better," Oscar said gruffly. "You knew that Proteus was the caretaker—the shepherd of the sea creatures —he was also a prophet who could see the future."

"Yes. I should have known better. When I did understand, I liked the name. So now, I am Charles Proteus Steinmetz."

"And that name will become famous. Don't forget," Oscar teased, "I promised the immigration officials that you were a genius."

Carl was suddenly serious. "It is not the name but the life that must count for something. A life devoted to science—for it is science that discovers truth."

\*      \*      \*

"Won't you change your mind? Louisa told me to ask you again," Oscar said.

Charles Steinmetz looked across at his roommate who was stacking books in neat piles on their worktable. Tomorrow Oscar was going to be married. The shelves which they had built out of old wooden boxes were bare; Oscar's trunk was packed and ready for closing. His own had been sent up to Yonkers. Their room looked deserted, as if already belonging to strangers.

Oscar came around to his friend's side of the table. "We took an extra room in the apartment so you could live with us."

"And hasn't Louisa enough to put up with in you, without my careless ways?" The tone was light but Oscar was not deceived.

Charles did not like the breaks that came in his life. It was always hard for him to make his way with strangers. But he said, "I am going to like Yonkers. They have little hills that some even call the Alps. And the room Mr. Mueller has offered me is less than twenty minutes' walk to the plant."

With a final glance about the room, Charles picked up an armful of books. "It is time for me to go."

Oscar put an arm around his friend's shoulder. "I never had a brother," he thought. "In you, I found one."

"I will be in good time for the wedding tomorrow." Charles gripped Oscar's arm. "And we'll get together often."

Listening to his uneven step on the stairs, Oscar wanted to go after him. "How alone he must feel," Louisa had said. "Do you think he will ever marry? He has so much love to give—and he is so good with children. Helva and I have talked about it. A man like that must have a home."

It was true that the little hunchback, the son of a hunchback, had determined never to marry. He had said as much to Oscar once and then never spoke of the matter again. But, being Charles Steinmetz, he would somehow have a home and children around him. He would work it out in good time and in a way all his own. . . .

Charles found a letter in the downstairs mailbox from his stepsister, Clara. Hurrying to make the early train to Yonkers, he put the unopened letter in his pocket to read later on the train. On his rides up the Hudson to work he had been planning, as he eyed the river's traffic, the sort of place he would get for his father and Clara, when he could send for them. They would surely prefer Yonkers to the hustle and bigness of New York. He would take long walks with his father as they used to do in the woods outside Breslau. They would hike up the Palisades and climb Bear Mountain.

When he had found a seat on the train, Charles opened his letter. He had never felt very close to his stepsister but she usually wrote lively and rather long accounts of doings at home. This letter was short—only one page. He read it through, then with tightened heart read it over and over, unable to believe what she had written. Their father had fallen ill of a fever. *His last thought was for you. He spoke as if you were in the room. Then his strength left him.*

Was it true? The train jogged around the big curve and came to the full view of the Hudson for which Charles watched each morning, but he did not see the river. Beyond the windowpane he saw a stooped, workworn figure with a hunched back and clear eyes full of understanding. He felt his father's arms about him, whispering, *"My son."* He was not to see his father again.

In the shop, working on drawings for an electric water pump Rudolph Eickemeyer had designed, Charles remembered about Oscar and the wedding tomorrow. "I must get through tomorrow without letting anyone know," he thought. "I will not dim their happiness."

Eickemeyer liked to arrange his daily visits with the workmen so that he reached the drafting room last. He had fallen into the habit of lingering for a talk with his young draftsman.

Today he had a serious matter to take up with Charles. All of them had come to depend on his mathematical skill for any difficult calculations. In his long years, the inventor thought he had found no one quite like young Steinmetz. He had an extraordinary mind and energy—yes, perhaps in his crippled body the rare energy and single-minded purpose of genius.

Taking a seat on a workbench near Charles' drafting board, the gray-bearded, aging man leaned over to examine the drawing. "I see you are nearly done."

"This pump will be useful to farmers," Charles answered, but he spoke without his usual zest.

Rudolph Eickemeyer told him of the successful run they had made yesterday in the electric streetcar. "Too bad you couldn't be there, Charles. It was quite a triumph."

"Yes?" Charles could feel the letter like a weight in his pocket.

"Now that we have solved the problem of the streetcar motor," Eickemeyer was saying, "we can turn to a bigger problem. We need power stations that can send electricity over long distances. This cannot be done with direct current."

Charles made no reply.

"You know that I have been working on a motor of a new type, one that uses alternating current instead of direct current. For some time I have been making experiments with alternating current in my small laboratory at home. So far it has been rather hit or miss,"

Eickemeyer went on. "The time has come to go at this research in more systematic fashion. We intend to set up a lab, here at the plant."

"A research laboratory?" Charles was listening now.

"Exactly. We will need someone to give full time to this work. How would you feel about undertaking this?" the older man saw the eager look returning in his draftsman's eyes.

"Yes, I will do it."

Work . . . There remained the blessing of work.

# A Laboratory of His Own

❧ THE DRAFTY ROOM IN THE LOFT next door was certainly not much to look at. But it was big and when the workmen finished cutting the door through for an entrance from the plant it would do very well for a research laboratory. There was a rusty wash-basin in one corner and a pot-bellied stove for heating in winter. A tall window in the back framed a view of the ever-changing Palisades.

Charles did not wait for the door to be cut. He kept racing up and down the stairway, enlisting everyone he could find to help him carry the odd assortment of wires, storage batteries, test tubes and motor parts he'd need for equipment.   For a worktable he had a drafting board with a stool to kneel on.

Several of Mr. Eickemeyer's inventions stood against the wall—among them the motor for an elevator he had designed for his friend, Mr. Otis.

Mr. Eickemeyer spent as much time as his failing health permitted in the laboratory. The loft became a friendly, happy place.

Rudolph Eickemeyer had sketched the plan for a motor using alternating current.   However, when the inventor came into the laboratory, he saw that instead of blueprints Charles' worktable was covered with numberless sheets of neat figures.

Charles pointed to a row of spoiled motors. They had failed to pass the test.   As each model failed, it was put aside and another, somewhat different in design, was begun.

"We are getting nowhere with this hit-or-miss system.   'Try and fail' is very wasteful. I've turned to mathematics," Charles said a little apologetically.

Rudolph Eickemeyer ran his long fingers through his beard, his brows drawn together. "True, we are working in the dark.   But we have no choice."

Engineers all over the country were doing the same, he said, for that matter in Europe also. This new motor, using alternating current, was clearly the machine of the future. The older type motor, using direct current, was more dependable for what it could do, tasks requiring low voltage and short distances, but it was limited.

Modern industry demanded machines that could develop high speed quickly and transmit electric power over long distances. Only alternating current could do this; yet no one, so far, had been able to make a reliable AC machine.

"We must find the answer," Charles said. "We ought to know what an AC motor will do *before* we build it, not after. Not the motor alone, but transformers and generators could be planned ahead if we understood the general principles—the natural laws—by which their performance is governed. We must learn the habits of iron and steel when they meet with electric current."

Eickemeyer sighed. "What you say is true. Alternating current is unpredictable. The main problem seems to be that we know so little about how magnetism works. It is in the magnetic core of the motors that the trouble starts. The metal doesn't stand up."

"The relation of magnetism to alternating current—," Charles interrupted. "You and I know that is the key."

The inventor smiled. "I have been studying magnets and their use in electrical work for ten years," he said. "I began it as a hobby when Graham Bell's telephone was new. I have developed something I call my 'magnetic bridge.' It tests the magnetic quality of a piece of iron, nickel or other metal as simply as you weigh a loaf of bread on a household scale."

"I see," Charles said with a sparkle in his eyes. "Can you bring your magnetic bridge here to the laboratory, Mr. Eickemeyer? We need to find out the best type of metal to use in making this next motor."

For the next week Charles tested every piece of scrap metal in the plant on Eickemeyer's magnetic bridge. He made a table of the findings. He poured over books and covered sheets of paper with calculations.

Will Egbert, who had come into the laboratory as a helper, grew impatient. He was a practical machinist and he wanted to build machines.

"By figuring, we save time in the end,"

Charles insisted. "It takes the head as well as the hand to conquer nature."

Mr. Eickemeyer looked over the notes Charles had written out.

"This will prove a real help," he agreed. "But the main problem remains. We know so little about what makes the magnetic current leak off as it does."

"There must be a natural law governing magnetic loss," Charles answered.

The inventor shrugged. "Most engineers doubt that such a uniform law can be set down."

"But everything is subject to natural law. Our problem is to find it." Charles smiled. "Mathematics can help us."

He showed the older man two series of tables and charts worked out by other scientists. "The puzzling thing," young Steinmetz explained, "is that the two sets of tables do not agree. When I plot them on a chart, the curves are not the same shape. It is very confusing. So we must work out our own set of tables on the magnetic loss in AC motors. Somewhere in the figures is hidden the answer we are seeking."

As soon as the director left, Will Egbert came over. "Look here, Mr. Steinmetz, what's this magnetism you were talking about? What's it got to do with motors?"

Steinmetz put aside his figuring. It was important for people like Will to understand.

"Not even the wisest men in science, Will, can tell us much about magnetism. The ancients long ago discovered that certain metals like iron, lodestone and even nickel had a power that seemed to them magic, the property of attracting other metals to them. This magnetic quality could be transferred by rubbing or tapping an iron magnet to another piece of metal. Surely you remember playing with magnets when you were a boy."

"Yeah," Will said. "And in school they talked about the compass with its magnetic needle that always points toward the North Pole. What's it got to do with my motors?"

Charles had begun to dismantle a motor while they talked. "Scientists have called the earth itself a giant magnet," he went on. "We know the whole universe is constantly moving. It gives off energy in varying forms of fire, heat, electricity, rainfall, or shooting stars. There are many other forms of energy in nature. Magnetism is one of the greatest. It operates in ways we are only beginning to understand."

"How about lightning? When it strikes?"

"Yes, above all, lightning. But this is a wild, untamed force." Charles Steinmetz paused, thinking of the night on shipboard when he looked forward to the day when man would understand lightning. "Someday we may tame it—and then . . . Oh, it's a great age, Will—a great time to be alive."

"What does magnetism have to do with electricity and motors?" Will persisted. "I know that the core of the electric motor is an iron magnet. Does this mean that magnetism and electricity are the same thing?"

"A very keen question, Will." Charles was pleased. "Many leading scientists are asking the same thing. This much we know; magnetism and electricity are closely related, powerful forces. I suspect that in good time scientists will discover that they are two forms of the same thing."

"Gee whiz, Mr. Steinmetz," Will looked at his hands. "You mean I carry electricity in my body? And you say everything is in motion, even this lab? Gee whiz!"

As Will went about his work, Charles Steinmetz was thinking that he must gather up a few textbooks to lend this nineteen-year-old mechanic. "When I see Oscar and Louisa next Sunday I will tell them of my promising pupil," Charles said to himself, as he went back to his figures.

But Charles did not make his usual visit to the young married couple that Sunday. On Friday afternoon Rudolph Eickemeyer stopped again at the laboratory.

"Mrs. Eickemeyer and I would be pleased if you could join us for dinner on Sunday," he said with a formal bow that reminded Charles of European ways.

Looking after the great man, as he walked back to his plant, Charles wondered if he had thanked him properly. Since he had first come to Yonkers to live with the Muellers, he had been hearing about "Sundays at Seven Oaks," the Eickemeyer house.

Mr. Mueller was occasionally invited to this gathering of famous scientists around the Eickemeyer's dinner table. But Charles had never expected—as he walked past the beautiful, red brick house—to be invited to Seven Oaks to meet such distinguished company.

He would have to write Oscar to explain. He could hear his friend grumble to Louisa. They had not made many new ties . . . Somehow they had not learned, as he had, to fit into the life of bustling America. But they would not really miss him. They had each other.

That Sunday at Seven Oaks was the first of many. Charles found the talk around the long, oak dining table interesting and sometimes exciting. Here it was that he first heard of the big, new company that was being formed, The General Electric. This would combine Thomas Edison's Lighting Plant in Manhattan with other companies in other parts of the state. Many men working together would tame this mysterious force, would harness electricity.

At the Eickemeyer table, too, he experienced the first puzzled silence when he happened to mention Galois' idea of a hundred years before —the device of calculating difficult things by means of imaginary numbers.

"Galois?" Mr. Olds, an important scientist said. "I never heard of him." Nor had any of the others. Could it be the use of imaginary numbers—such as the square root of minus one—was all but forgotten?

That night Charles pulled out all his old notebooks. In an early one, from the University at Breslau, he found what he wanted. He had made the notes in shorthand five years ago but he read them with ease. The symbol $\sqrt{-1}$, thought up by a Frenchman when the United States was scarcely a nation was going to produce power for that nation such as the world had never seen!

\* \* \*

Not long afterward, Charles Steinmetz left the laboratory early and traveled with Rudolph Eickemeyer down to New York. He was going, for the first time, to a meeting of the American Institute of Electrical Engineers.

Many of the members glanced at the elderly, dignified inventor, over six feet in height, as he walked to his seat in the crowded hall. Then they stared at the little hunchback who was half running to keep up with him.

"That is Eickemeyer, the inventor."

"Yes, I know. But who is the strange little fellow with him?"

"Some foreigner. German, I think."

"Is he an engineer?"

"A new draftsman at Eickemeyer's plant."

"Not an electrical engineer? Then what is he doing here?"

"The Old Man brought him. Steinmetz, I think the name is. Charles Steinmetz."

"Never heard of him."

The Institute's main session was given over to a paper by a leading engineer, Thornton Reid, on the problem of alternating current. Charles made notes. After the speaker had finished, he raised his hand.

"Is it permit' to ask questions?"

"Why, yes. If any occur to you."

"They occur."

The chairman nodded toward Mr. Reid, who stood up to answer. "What is your question?"

"Why did you stop so soon? Why did you not deal with the higher frequencies?"

Thornton Reid looked surprised. "It did not seem necessary. It would have made the work too complicated."

"But without this," Charles persisted, "is not your study of alternating current incomplete?"

Members of the audience were turning around for a good look at this newcomer. The young man with the strong German accent did not seem to understand. An electrical engineer was not accustomed to push his calculations further. Beyond this was a realm of higher mathematics that few ventured into, not even such a man as Thornton Reid.

Someone in the audience rose. "Perhaps the new member," he said with a slight sneer in his voice, "would like to work out these calculations himself."

Rudolph Eickemeyer flushed. "My young friend, Charles Steinmetz, is unknown to most of you here, so I must tell you that he is a mathematician of unusual gifts. I would second the proposal if Mr. Reid is agreeable to it. Let us ask—Charles P. Steinmetz"— he paused. "You may have cause someday to remember the name. Let us request Mr. Steinmetz to work out the calculations and present his findings in a paper at our next session."

The chairman asked, "Mr. Steinmetz, will you accept?"

Charles nodded. "Yes," he said in a calm, matter-of-fact voice. "If you wish me, I will do it."

\*       \*       \*

"This motor is *kaput*." Will set the motor they had finished testing against the wall which was lined with failures.

Charles looked up from his figuring. "We know the trouble has to do with the magnetic circuit. As the motor runs, there is a leakage of current. The iron frame takes up the charge. The whole motor overheats, and we have failed again. We will continue to fail until we find out the relation between the strength of the magnet used and the rate at which the motor loses its power."

Will came over by the desk. "So that's what all the figuring's about?"

"Exactly. Through these figures, I'm tracking down this tricky old fellow, magnetism. Once we find out the law that governs magnetic loss, we can build motors according to plan."

"How do you mean there's a law?"

His supervisor was looking at him. "Will, you make a habit of asking questions."

"Is that bad?"

"No. It's good. Even if you are a nuisance sometimes, never stop asking. In fact, this is how science goes ahead. Men keep asking questions. They get answers, they share their findings. This leads to more questions."

"You mean there's no end?"

"In science there are only beginnings. Milestones along the way. Galileo. Franklin with his kite. Edison and his lamp. Nikola Tesla. By the way, the first patent taken out on a motor in this country was by a blacksmith, Thomas Davenport."

Will grinned. "You mean, there's hope for me? But this book you gave me on electricity, it's hard going. This man can't explain things the way you do!"

"Make notes on the hard part of it," Charles told him, "and we'll have a try at it. Now, back to your question. We do not know much yet about alternating current but we shall find out. Mr. Eickemeyer and I have been working on it for months. And many other people besides."

"You'll find out all right."

Charles Steinmetz took a pad and began sketching the main parts of a motor. "Here, at the motor's core is the magnet. Surrounding it, is the space called the magnetic field. In motors using direct current, the magnetism remains always the same. It remains constant."

"Of course—because the current always flows in one direction," Will said.

"In these AC motors, the electric current flows from A to Z, then changes over, like this, and flows back from Z to A, then again from A to Z and so on faster than one-two-three."

"Faster than my dog could wag his tail," Will murmured.

"The magnetic current also shifts back and

forth," Charles said. "When this happens, the motor consumes its own power, which is very wasteful. The rest you know: the machine overheats and soon breaks down."

"Yeah—goes crazy. And we've built another motor that won't last—right back where we started."

"Not exactly." Charles went over to his worktable. "We are on the track. We shall find a way to design a motor that does not suffer from this strain. Engineers call this loss of power by a long word from the Greek, meaning loss. The word is *hysteresis*. You might as well learn it, Will, because you'll hear a lot of it from now on."

He ruffled the sheets of paper covered with figures. "I am trying to find a way of calculating this loss—this hysteresis. When we can figure the measure of loss, we'll know how hot the iron core of your motor will get under given conditions. Then we shall build AC motors, transformers or any kind of electrical machines and know ahead of time just how they will stand up. No more try and fail and try again!"

"You make it clear. It sounds easy," Will said, "even when it isn't. How do you spell that word, Mr. Steinmetz—hysteresis?"

Charles Steinmetz laughed and turned back to his figuring. The boy stood for a moment watching him, then sauntered into the shop to repair a hat machine.

While he was gone, Rudolph Eickemeyer came into the lab. "Well, Charles, have you worked out the calculations for Thornton Reid?"

Steinmetz took the completed paper from a drawer.

The older man studied it carefully. "This will please Thornton very much. They will ask you to read it at the Institute's next session."

"With my accent?"

"When they understand what these findings mean, they'll forget the accent." The inventor picked up the other sheets of figures on which Charles had been working.

"What are these equations you have here?"

Charles flushed. "I am trying to work out a formula—a method. Take this chart now—" Charles warmed to his subject.

An hour later the inventor sighed. "Charles, I am not the mathematician you are. You are getting beyond me. But keep it up. Something good will come of it."

\*    \*    \*

"Something sure will come of it," Will told his girl, Susan. "Something big maybe."

"Poor, lonely little man." Susan was looking up at the lighted window glowing in the darkness. "He is up there alone. Night after night when we go by the plant, he's up there."

"Nobody needs to feel sorry for Charles Steinmetz," Will said. "He may be little— if he is, he's a little giant. And being lonesome is not what's driving him to work so hard."

"What then?"

Will was at a loss how to put it. To most people work was one thing, fun another.

For the little hunchback, work and fun were one and the same. "That's how it ought to be for everybody, Will," Steinmetz had explained. "Some day it will be. Every man will choose work to his liking."

"You mean work will be fun for everybody? But how, Mr. Steinmetz? For most people, work is plain drudgery."

"True, Will. Now, only a few are lucky. But you have pride in work. When you make a neat repair job on a machine, you feel set up."

"Right. But that's not the whole of it."

"True, Will. The majority of men and

women have to keep their noses pretty close to the grindstone. Long hours. Low pay. Fear of lay-offs. But things will change. Even now we see them changing. Machines are taking over the heaviest work, freeing men of burdens. Soon hours will be cut down."

Will tried to explain to Susan. "Just mark what I tell you. That little fellow is on the track of something big."

"You sound downright proud of him," the girl said. "Like he belonged to you, was kinfolk or something."

Will was smiling at her in the darkness. "You know, he believes that. 'All men are brothers.' Sure, a lot of people *say* it, but with him it's fact." Will nodded toward the window. "When we come down to it, Sue, that's what drives him."

"You mean why he works so hard? To find out things, make the good times come nearer? I am glad you work for him, Will. Look how he helps you."

"He believes in people. Everybody." Will's laugh had a catch in it. "Even guys like me."

# The Little Giant

⊂⊐ LATE IN THE SUMMER, EDWARD Mueller stepped into Mr. Eickemeyer's office and closed the door behind him. "Maybe you will speak to Steinmetz?"

"Is anything wrong?"

"Night and day he is here at the lab."

"Yes, I know. He is very intent on finding this law on magnetic loss."

"But he is driving himself beyond bounds. He's not eating right. Some nights his bed is not slept in. My wife made me promise to speak to you! She is very fond of our young

123

roomer—he has become like an older son to us."

Rudolph Eickemeyer agreed to speak with his assistant. "Not that he will listen." Had *he* listened when working on an idea? To his wife? To doctors, anyone?

In the laboratory, Eickemeyer found Stephen Fields, Otis and a couple of engineers from the nearby carpet shop gathered around Steinmetz, as he weighed samples of iron on the magnetic bridge. It was not unusual to find engineers from other plants and even from out of town dropping in to see how the magnetic bridge worked or to examine the new AC motor or to hear some of Steinmetz's uncanny magic with figures.

"This Eickemeyer bridge lets us measure the amount of magnetism each of these materials will carry," Charles was explaining. "Cast-iron, widely used now, will carry only about one half as much magnetism as wrought-iron. Cast steel lies between cast-iron and wrought-iron. Some grades of cast steel will take magnetism as well as wrought-iron, and hold the charge better."

The experiments done, Charles appeared restless. As soon as the visitors were gone, he turned to Rudolph Eickemeyer. "It works! Our formula works!"

"What are you talking about?"

Charles took a thick set of papers from his desk. "Please, I would like it very much if you would go over these." He turned the pages quickly. "The method, the tests you know. Here! Here are the findings. And the tables and charts."

Rudolph Eickemeyer went over them several times. "A good deal of this math is beyond me."

Charles explained at some length. "I used Ewing's table of figures on magnetic losses. After months of studying and working them over and trying out various methods, I think we have the secret. Roughly it is this: every time we double a motor's magnetic power, the hysteresis or magnetic loss becomes three times as great. That gave me the key to the formula."

"But this means you have solved the problem! You have discovered the law of hysteresis?"

The younger man nodded, his face alight. "Now engineers can design and make AC machines without guesswork. They can know in advance how strong a magnetic current to use."

After testing out the new formula on several alternating current motors, Rudolph Eickemeyer was convinced.

"Charles, you have cleared up a problem that has stumped every manufacturer of alternating current machines. The whole industry will be grateful."

"Not I—we. You and Mr. Fields and Will —"

"You mean I helped?" Will dropped a coil of wire in his excitement.

"You helped build and test out the motors, didn't you?" Charles Steinmetz was laughing for the joy of it. Will and the older man joined in. "After all these months of work," Charles said, "how about it? Doesn't this call for a celebration?"

\*      \*      \*

That night Charles took the train to Harlem. He couldn't wait until Sunday to share his triumph with Oscar and Louisa.

"To push back the boundaries of knowledge," he said, when he had explained what he'd been working on—"that is what we have hoped for, isn't it? And my discovery will be practical, too. Knowledge should be put to use. That is something I have learned from Rudolph Eickemeyer. We'll run streetcars without wearing out our friends, the horses. We'll put power to work on the farms, in homes. Someday, Louisa, you will press a button and pouf! your week's wash will be done . . ."

"It's wonderful, Charles." Oscar tried to throw himself wholeheartedly into his friend's mood.

But Charles sensed something. He looked from Oscar to Louisa and back again. "Tell me," he demanded. "I have gone on too long about my own affairs."

"I have been meaning to talk to you," Oscar answered. "Louisa and I are discouraged with the life here. We are going back to Switzerland."

"Leave America? Oscar, you can't. I know things are not perfect. Even I see many people like your Uncle Josef—people who care more about getting ahead than about doing a good job . . . But the others—the thousands of others . . ."

"Come with us, Carl; we are your family—" Louisa put out her hand. "When we have children they will love you as they do us. Think of the pretty little street in

Zurich—and now that Bismarck is out of power in Germany you can go to visit the places you love. Here, life is too hard."

"America is a challenge." Charles stared at his friends, unbelieving. "Europe or here, all life is a struggle. We can't run away from it."

"Helva and Erik were right," Oscar answered, slowly. "They said you would not leave. They think we are asking the impossible of life and running from place to place to find it."

"I do not think that," Charles said. "You will find ways to make your lives count in the old country—but my work is here. This is my country!"

*     *     *

"It is raining hard! Take this umbrella and wear your rubbers." The Mueller children stood by, while Charles pulled on his clumsy rubber boots and rolled up his trouser cuffs to protect them from the downpour. Then he set out for the train that would take him to New York.

He was going to the quarterly meeting of the American Institute of Electrical Engineers. Inside his jacket, safe from the rain, was the paper that he was to give before that body. When he finished reading those hundred and seventy-eight pages everyone would understand about the law of hysteresis.

His mind was entirely on the presentation of the paper. Without remembering to take off his rubber boots or pull down the cuffs of his trousers, he limped into the hall and onto the platform. He looked like a dwarf out of a Grimm's fairy tale.

However, the audience forgot his appearance when he had read a few pages. This strange little man, in his awkward English, was giving the answers to questions plaguing every engineer. Charles Proteus Steinmetz, three years after arriving as an immigrant at Castle Garden, had solved one of the major problems of the electrical age!

It was after midnight when the reading came to an end, but no one had stirred from his seat. The president of the society rose.

"The American Institute of Electrical Engineers may well congratulate itself on this paper," he said. "Mr. Steinmetz has put into our hands the key to unlock the full treasure-house of electric power."

Thornton Reid and Rudolph Eickemeyer were among the first to crowd forward to shake Charles' hand.

The men stood around after the session was over, discussing Steinmetz' findings.

"His paper is a classic," Thornton Reid declared.

"Don't tell me you understood it. The mathematics was way over my head."

"Trouble is, nobody understands it. Not even Eickemeyer."

"Never mind. If this formula works, we will know enough to use it."

"And how! I can't wait till I get back to the plant to give it a try."

FORMULA

$\sqrt{-1}$ to represent the time dimensions in A.C. calculations

## *"Life Brings Many Changes"*

"MR. STEINMETZ, THERE'S A LONG distance call from the Chicago plant. They want to know if the new transformer is still held up. Mr. Eickemeyer asked me to bring you the message," Will Egbert said. "He is to call them back. They say they are waiting to start production. They have an order for 900 transformers from Midwest States Light and Power Company."

Charles Steinmetz looked up from his figuring. "Tell them we'll need more time on the transformer. I do not know how much."

"They seem in a hurry."

"Who isn't? Rush—all the time rush! But science will not be hurried."

"They say they can't go ahead without the transformer." Will hesitated. "Mr. Steinmetz, exactly what is a transformer? I mean what on earth does it do?"

Generators and dynamos he understood pretty well. They were machines that changed mechanical energy into electrical energy. Machines used the energy of coal or gasoline, or waterfalls to make electricity. Motors converted electrical energy into motion or mechanical energy, to drive wheels or other machines.

Two years had gone by since Charles Steinmetz had solved the problem of magnetic current and Will, along with everybody in the Eickemeyer plant, had grown accustomed to seeing one successful machine turned out, after another. But what were these transformers everybody was suddenly clamoring for?

Steinmetz pointed to the map of the United States on the wall. "Today we want to send electric current long distances. Take this Midwest States Company. Its power station is located here in the Illinois coal region, but it will send light and power to cities many miles away. Direct current can not travel such distances, but alternating current can.

"This is where transformers come in. The voltage, necessary for transmitting electricity such long ways, is far too high for practical use. There had to be a way of stepping the high voltage down at the point where the electric power would be put to use. The machine that converts the high voltage current to the 110 volts that factories, homes and stores are equipped to use—that's the transformer. Any questions?"

"Several." Will grinned. "But I'd better take your message back to Mr. Eickemeyer before I get fired."

When his assistant returned to the lab, Steinmetz was walking up and down the floor.

"Will, we are caught between Scylla and Charybdis."

"Between what?"

"We are in a fix. Light and power systems developing fast. Plants multiplying. Fine! But here's the rub. Engineers all over the country are making machines based on alternating current: motors, generators, transformers. But they wear out because we still don't know how alternating current really works. Old AC is an unruly character. Undependable."

"You'll track him down." Will began cleaning the shelves of dead batteries, broken test tubes and junked motor parts. They needed space for the transformers they were testing.

"Funny thing, Will. You remember when we discovered how to control the magnetic circuit? We thought we had solved everything when the law of hysteresis was formulated. It has simply added to our problem."

"How's that?"

"It cleared the way for use of alternating current machines. But the machines don't work right."

Will loaded a wagon with discarded parts. "It is like you told me. In science you ask a question. Find the answer. Then up pops another question."

Charles smiled. "See that you remember when you are away from here in college."

Will stopped short. "You didn't mean what you said the other day, did you—that I had it in me to be an engineer? I told Susie and she thought it was wonderful—but I was sure you were joking."

Charles Steinmetz fumbled in his pocket and drew out an official looking letter.

"I have arranged for you to go to the Polytechnic Institute upstate if you pass the examination—and you will pass it." He thrust the letter into the hand of the astonished young mechanic. "As you see—everything is paid for," he added.

"Gee whiz, Mr. Steinmetz—how can I thank you?"

"You are not to thank me—what should I do with the money Mr. Eickemeyer pays me? I have no family, no young brothers to educate. You will make a good scientist and of this, the country has need."

*       *       *

The summer went by and Will left for the Polytechnic Institute. Still, Charles Steinmetz spent long hours kneeling at his worktable. Sometimes people found him sitting crosslegged on the table itself, head bent over his charts.

Finally, one Sunday, he appeared again at Seven Oaks, gay and high spirited, full of jokes. When the rest of the company had gone, he brought out a thick bundle of papers.

"Please," he said to Mr. Eickemeyer, "would you look over these?"

Rudolph Eickemeyer shook his head over the pages and pages of figuring. "Since working with you, Charles," he said, "I have learned a new respect for mathematics. But I must ask you to translate. What are these strange equation with $\sqrt{-1}$, the square root of minus one?"

"Do you remember once at your dinner table I spoke of Galois and his imaginary numbers? His work has been neglected, but with it as a starting point I am working out a new kind of table. The old methods of figuring alternating current do not work."

"True. All equations worked out so far are very complicated. And inaccurate."

"What has us stumped is that AC never stays the same. It keeps changing. How can we measure such a shifty fellow?"

Charles pointed to his worksheets. "With ordinary numbers we can measure three dimensions, length, width, height. But since AC keeps changing its flow 120 times a second, we need to measure a fourth dimension: time. This is why equations up to now have been so complicated and useless. So I have found a simpler method."

"Come now, Charles. *Better* probably, but hardly simpler!"

"Let me explain. In math we have two series of numbers, ordinary and imaginary numbers. Please, Mr. Eickemeyer don't start shaking your head."

"Who uses imaginary numbers nowadays?"

"But they are useful. See, I have used the imaginary number $\sqrt{-1}$ to represent the time dimension in AC calculations. And since the proof of the pudding is in the eating—here it is. The formula works." Steinmetz went over his calculations with the inventor.

Mr. Eickemeyer studied the figures intently. The sun went down and Charles reached up and turned on the electric light bulb. After another hour, Mrs. Eickemeyer came into the silent study, set down a tray with tea and cookies. They went untasted. At last, Mr. Eickemeyer raised his eyes from the desk.

"This is as important as the law of hysteresis!" he exclaimed. "But Charles, you must be prepared. When you report this method and these findings in your next paper to the American Institute of Electrical Engineers no one will understand it. No one."

Charles found this hard to accept. But the older man proved to be right. The paper was acclaimed, but engineers left the hall with a baffled look.

Riding home on the train Rudolph Eickemeyer said, "It was an historic paper, Charles.
But how many understood it?"

Charles was thinking it over. "It is not
their fault they did not understand. Imaginary numbers have been forgotten. This
means I must find a way to make it clear."
He would begin collecting his papers and
notes and start work on a book explaining this
method. But he would need time to write a
book. Perhaps there was no opportunity, if
there was something new at the plant?

"What research are we going to start on
next?" Charles asked.

For a time Rudolph Eickemeyer stared out
of the train window. "I am no longer a
young man. My health is not what it was."

He raised an unsteady hand to his beard.
Charles realized suddenly what others had
known for a long time: Rudolph Eickemeyer
was an old, old man.

"You have no need to work so hard. Mr.
Fields and Mr. Mueller and I, we'll manage.
We will bring problems to you. You will
advise us as always."

Rudolph Eickemeyer was staring at the
river. "I have not wanted to tell you this. I
must retire, Charles. General Electric, the

company up at Schenectady, has made a good
offer for the plant. And for my patents."

"You are selling the plant? Retiring?"
Charles could not believe it.

Rudolph Eickemeyer smiled. "It is not as
bad as you think. General Electric has asked
for you. Their's is a coming firm. You will
go far with them."

"I have been working with you." Charles
spoke as if to himself. "I could not ask more."

Rudolph Eickemeyer began talking quietly
about the future before the electrical industry.
His companion did not answer.

"Charles, life brings many changes. We
have to face them."

The younger man nodded. These breaks
in life, was there no end to them? His father,
Oscar, and now, Rudolph Eickemeyer. This
man had grown to be like a father to him.
The lab had become home. His friends, the
Muellers, who had taken him into their
family. Sundays at Seven Oaks. All was
coming to an end.

"My wife and I are leaving Yonkers for a
time," the old man said. "The doctors think
the warm winters in Florida may help."

Charles looked up. "How soon?"

"In the next weeks."

Mr. W. E. Rice, chief engineer with General Electric, traveled down from Schenectady to the Eickemeyer laboratory and asked for its director, Charles P. Steinmetz. He was startled to find a young man sitting cross-legged on a worktable. Almost a dwarf.

"I am Charles Steinmetz. Won't you sit down?"

Edwin Rice wondered if there could be a mistake. Was this cripple in the old knitted jacket really the genius he had been led to expect? *It's as important to get Charles Steinmetz as the patents,* the heads of General Electric had said among themselves when the sale was being arranged.

"Tell me about your new design for turbines, Mr. Rice. I believe you plan to use them in the first power station at Niagara Falls?" Charles said.

As soon as they began to talk, Edwin Rice forgot his earlier doubts. Here was a man who spoke with quiet authority. In his piercing but kindly glance there was a strange power.

"When you come to us, Mr. Steinmetz, we want to make full use of your mathematical abilities. You will work in the Calculating

Department.   Your time and working conditions will be whatever you desire."

"The Calculating Department.   Very good."

"Your main work will be on dynamos for Niagara Falls."

"Excellent!   Use of such water power to generate electricity opens up great possibilities," Charles said.

"However, before you come to Schenectady —as soon as Mr. Eickemeyer can spare you," Edwin Rice went on, "there is a small problem in one of our Massachusetts factories, at Lynn. Can you go there?"

"Of course, as you wish."

"Now, Mr. Steinmetz, about salary —"

Charles Steinmetz cut him short.   "You will give me, I am sure enough to live on?"

"Of course."

"Then that is settled."

Mr. Rice was astounded.   Perhaps this twenty-eight-year-old mathematician had not understood.

"You tell me I will have enough to live on. What more does a person need?"   With a friendly wave of a hand, Charles dismissed the subject.   "But one thing I must tell you.   I will require some time to complete my research work and my book on alternating current."

Charles Steinmetz glanced at his visitor with a sudden boyish grin. "I am beginning to fear that one book will not do it. This AC fellow has quite a history. It may take two, even three volumes to deal with him."

# Work Is Not Enough

CHARLES HAD COMPLETED HIS stay in Massachusetts and was quite at home in Schenectady. At the General Electric plant he had plunged at once into important work on the huge turbines for Niagara's water-power station.

He had had time to work on his book as well. The first volume was almost ready for the printer, when the chief engineer stopped at his desk one morning.

"The turbines for the Niagara station are ready, Mr. Steinmetz. We trust no one but you to install them. Can you leave for Niagara Falls tomorrow?"

"Of course," Charles replied. For a man like himself it was easy enough to travel. You just turned the key on the door of your rented room. Whether you were here, or there, made no difference to anyone.

Never in all his years had Charles Steinmetz been so alone or so lonely. The work at General Electric was fine—it was important and exciting. But there was no one to share it with; no Oscar, no Rudolph Eickemeyer— not even a boy like Will Egbert, eager for life and for learning.

Standing by the falls the next day, Charles was impressed by their beauty quite as much as by the gigantic energy they offered. But the crowds of awed sight-seers made him feel even more alone. Families chattering happily together. Elderly couples and young lovers. A bride in her new finery walking sedately along the path and stealing now and then a proud glance at the young husband at her side . . .

Charles turned away and walked back to his hotel. "Tomorrow I will start installing the turbines," he said to himself. "At least there is always work.  To make your life count, that is the thing."

But work by itself, even important work, was not enough.

\*    \*    \*

"Don't bother to unpack," Steinmetz was told when he returned to Schenectady.  General Electric was sending him as one of its crew of engineers to set up and supervise its exhibit at the Chicago World's Fair.

Ernst Berg, one of the young men in the Calculating Department, was going along. "Maybe they think you rate a vacation," Ernst said.  "More likely, if anything breaks down on our model electric railway, they count on your figuring a way to fix it in a hurry."

After helping the mechanics set up the miniature electric elevated railway in the General Electric building, Carl had time to explore the rest of the magnificent buildings and exhibits.  "We are looking at the future!" he said to Ernst Berg.  How good it was to have someone to share these wonders!

However, when the Fair was opened to the public, Charles spent more and more time in the G. E. building.  Here, among the display of electric motors and turbines, the little train running on its elevated platform was always

the center of an admiring crowd. Charles
loved to stand among the children listening to
their shrill cries of delight at the perfectly designed electric engine, pulling passenger and
freight cars around and around the tracks.
And the children talked to him as if he were
one of themselves.

On the last day of his stay, a tall, dark-eyed
boy ran up to him. "Carl! It is you? Don't
you remember me, Carl? I am Pierre Lefrak.
I might have known I would find you admiring a miniature train!"

"Little Pierre!" Carl took him by both
hands. "But, in four years, how you've
grown!"

Laughing, both talking at once, they
walked over to the boy's parents. The Lefraks
were living on a small farm near Milwaukee,
they said, and hoped Carl would do them the
honor of making them a visit. Pierre was in
high school. "He plans to become one of
these new-fangled scientific farmers," Jean
Lefrak said, with a proud glance at his son.

"You are working for General Electric?"
Pierre asked. "Do you still study the stars?"

"When I get time."

"The stars look big in the sky over our
farm. Sometime I look up at them, Carl,

and think of our talks on our ocean voyage."

Pierre's mother asked about Oscar. "He returned with his wife to Europe," Charles explained. "He writes they are happier there. They have a little girl. They named her Carla—for me."

Jean Lefrak asked, "How do you find it here?"

"This country has been good to me."

"You have work with the big G. E.? You are lucky—an immigrant boy. Would they let you off this afternoon to go with us to the zoo? I remember that you like animals and the Chicago Zoo is famous."

Charles smiled. "They will let me—and I like animals. I like also to be with my friends."

It was a joyous afternoon and when he left them, Charles invited the Lefraks to come to see him at the General Electric plant if ever they were in Schenectady.

"Such a big plant, this G. E.," Jean Lefrak said, as they watched Charles hurry off to catch his train. "Looking for the little Steinmetz fellow, there, would be like looking for a needle in our haystack."

"You think so, Papa?" Pierre answered. "Maybe. But I would not be so sure."

Ernst Berg was already in their seat on the train when Charles came in.

"You look as if somebody gave you a million dollars," Ernst said with an amused glance at his companion.

"A million dollars—no. But somebody gave me an idea!" Charles settled himself near the window and considered how he could explain to Ernst Berg.

"I am a man without roots," he began. "A family man without a home or family. Work, I have, and work is the strong, firm warp of a life. But on this warp must be woven bright-colored patterns—friends, the laughter of children, animals, too."

He paused and looked up at Ernst with a mischievous twinkle in his eyes. "You know this afternoon I was at the zoo. And the children and the bears and I, we had our fun together."

"You like animals?" Ernst Berg sat up with sudden interest. "You never said so, at the plant. In the Calculating Department your head is so full of figures all of us stand in awe of you. Say—you'll have to come to see my dog and the rabbits my brother raises."

"You have a dog and rabbits?" Charles whipped out his notebook. "That's good.

They will be a beginning for our zoo! All the way down to the train I was thinking: why not a home of my own? With my own lab and place for a garden . . . And why not a zoo of my own to entice the children of the neighborhood?"

"Yes?" Ernst prompted, when Charles stopped short.

"Well, it was part of my idea—though you and your brother do not know me very well —except that on this journey we seem to have become friends . . ."

"Are you suggesting that we take a house together?" Ernst asked. "There's nothing I'd like better and I think I can speak for my brother, too."

## A Battle Royal Starting

⌁ THE HOUSEHOLD WHICH CHARLES and the Berg brothers set up on Liberty Street became the talk of the neighborhood. The young engineers turned the big downstairs room into a laboratory where they carried on noisy electrical experiments. They built a glass-roofed hothouse for rare plants. They filled the backyard with pens and cages for their odd pets.

"Nobody can deny the orchids the little Steinmetz man grows are beautiful and also the ferns, some taller than your head. But those animals!" the staid housewives exclaimed over their afternoon tea.

But the children welcomed the arrival of each new animal with wide-eyed interest. The zoo started with Ernst's long-legged hound and Eskil Berg's rabbits. Before they were even settled in the house, Ernst captured a young eagle in the woods. Charles added a pair of owls and a lusty three-foot alligator. He taught it several tricks which delighted the children when they stopped by on their way from school.

Another favorite was a very intelligent monkey called Jenny. There was also Benjy, the raccoon. Benjy had the run of the house, upstairs and down, until one day he feasted on the leg of lamb intended for Sunday dinner!

"The monthly grocery bill for your pets is higher than for the people," Mrs. Larson, the housekeeper protested.

"And why not?" Charles answered. "There are more of them."

Word of the zoo on Liberty Street spread and troops of school children came from various parts of town to wonder and ask questions. Charles was delighted. This was what he

hoped for—to have children around. He answered their questions with the same patience
he showed when training engineers at General
Electric in the use of his mathematical equations.

"He is by nature a teacher," Ernst said.

The Calculating Department, where Steinmetz was now in charge, had become a sort
of glorified classroom. Engineers from a distance as well as from the vast spread-out
buildings at the Schenectady plant came to
him to learn. "Steinmetz of G.E." was becoming a name to remember.

The last of the three volumes on "Alternating Current" had gone into print and Charles
was busy now on new problems. He worked
at home as often as at the plant for Edwin
Rice had been true to his promise; Steinmetz
was able to come and go as he pleased.

Lights burned late in the house. Hearing
a rumble and roar, the neighbors would turn
uneasily in their beds. "That little man is at
it again!" they'd say.

Mrs. Larson, the housekeeper, would find
fresh burns in the carpet and brown stains on
woodwork and furniture. Terrible smells
would hang over the room after one of
Charles' wild experiments.

The housekeeper threatened to give notice. "But then how can I leave?" she would say to her son. "Mr. Steinmetz is a gentle, good-natured man. He meets you with his shy look and says, 'I am sorry if I make you extra work. I promise to be more careful.' Next time he gets an idea, he does it again."

Finally, the lab was moved out to the stable. Here, friends from all over came to see what Charles Steinmetz was up to. New friends, like Mr. Thomas Edison. Old ones, like Michael Pupin and the Muellers from Yonkers. And Will Egbert going home after his first year at college.

Will looked over the place admiringly. "I have to see everything, so I can tell Susie. She worried about you that you wouldn't have a good time away from Yonkers. Wait till I tell her!"

"I suppose," Charles answered, "you make your good times if you must." *Go on and live, Carl*—that was what his father had said.

The good times were not all at Liberty Street. The Berg brothers and Charles took long tramps along the Mohawk River. In winter they went skiing on the hills. They made bicycling trips into the surrounding valleys and once they brought back to the zoo a young fawn that had lost its mother.

Most of all they enjoyed rowing and paddling. "We must have a boat," Ernst said. "We'll go partners."

"Yes, but it can't be just any boat," Charles answered with his usual enthusiasm. "It must be built to order." He whipped out his notebook and began sketching the design that came immediately to his mind.

The problem was to find someone to build it. He hunted up an old river man, a retired boat-builder.

"Mr. Joiner, will you build us this boat?"

"Can't. Gave up making boats long back."

Charles traveled out several times to persuade the old man. Once he had a design in his mind—whether for a complicated machine or for a simple boat that would go up shallow creeks, he could not rest until it became a reality.

"Can't build it. No good tools any more," Mr. Joiner repeated.

"We'll see you get tools. We'll pay you well. Whatever you think it is worth."

When the boat was launched the men spent Sundays exploring all the streams and creeks that fed the Mohawk. On a bluff above Viele Creek, Charles fell in love with a fine view.

"We could make a nice place here. A cabin for week ends." Charles took out his notebook. "I must find out who owns this spot."

"You are joking!" Eskil exclaimed.

But Charles didn't answer. He was busy with a sketch for an Alpine cabin. "It may take a little while to get started."

\*     \*     \*

Seven work-filled years rushed by before Charles' dream came true. It was in the late spring of the year that the electric underground railway was opened in New York, that the camp on Viele Creek was completed. Charles Steinmetz had accepted with calm, the success of the new marvelous subway power stations and all the great leap forward of electricity in industry. It was beyond his earlier imagining.

The natural laws governing magnetic circuits and alternating current had been set down in formulas, he said. It followed that ways would be found to put electrical power to the fullest use of mankind. But a house of his own—even a one-room cabin—where he could share with his friends the beauties of this American landscape: that was something that called for a celebration!

"We'll hire stagecoaches to make the trip and an orchestra to make music," he said to

Ernst. "And you and Eskil will make a bowl of your famous Swedish punch."

First Eskil, then Ernst had married and moved into homes of their own. Charles was alone again in the house on Liberty Street but the Bergs and their wives would surely come to the party.

When the date had been set, Charles went around the G. E. plant inviting the guests. There were so many people he wanted to ask that he had to engage another stagecoach.

"Now we have room for still a few more friends," he said to Ernst and glanced through the list of workers in his own department to see if there were any he had overlooked. He came to a new name—an assistant recently hired. "Who is this Roy Hayden?" he asked.

"He's the boy from Harvard. Don't you remember? He was studying law—his grandfather is a judge or something. Happened to read an article you wrote about electricity being the poetry and romance and adventure of today. Young Hayden gave up the idea of being a lawyer and came to Schenectady and got a job with G. E. He's not an engineer, just an assistant."

Next morning Charles stood at Roy Hayden's shoulder. "I am having a party at my cabin on Viele Creek. Please, I should like it, if you came along?"

On Saturday noon the stagecoaches started off through the streets of Schenectady.

"Give us a tune!" Charles cried to the musicians. "Something lively like Ta-ra-ra-boom-te-ray. Everybody sing!"

Charles noticed the young assistant sitting next to a pretty girl: Corinne Rost, the sister of one of the machinists who had worked on the power stations for the New York underground railway. Charles had met her one day when she came by the Liberty Street lab with her brother. While they pored over blue-prints for the dynamos, the girl had made friends with Benjy. This was why Charles remembered her. He was pleased, now, that the young man from Harvard had found a companion to talk to.

He thought no more about Roy Hayden until late evening when the party was almost over. It had been a wonderful day—in every way perfect—from the hour the pair of coaches had pulled up at Viele Creek with fiddles going and trumpet blaring.

"Here we are!" Charles had signaled the

drivers to stop. He watched with mischievous pleasure the puzzled looks of his guests.

Where was the camp? Charles stood by, until they spied the pointed roof of the cabin high above on the bluff. The unpainted cabin was completely hidden on three sides by trees. The side facing the creek hung out over the bluff supported by heavy timbers.

"Like Switzerland!" the guests said over and over and Charles sparkled with pleasure.

After hours of boating and swimming in the creek, Charles' friends gathered in the one-room cabin for a lavish spread. Then they danced while the musicians played waltzes and folktunes from the Old Country and American square dances.

At the close of the day, when the stage-coaches returned for the drive home, the guests noticed Charles had not climbed aboard. "Aren't you coming?"

"And miss Sunday, here in the woods? Which of you men are staying over with me? Eskil, how about it. Ernst?"

"Where'd we sleep? There is only one cot."

"We'll draw lots for it. The rest on the floor."

Seeing that no one volunteered, Roy Hayden spoke up. "I would like to, very much, Mr. Steinmetz. That is, if it's all right."

"Fine! First rate! Let the softies go back to town. We'll have a day in the open and get ready for next week-end. And I want to start a dam across the narrow bend of the creek. When I see water I am no better than a beaver!"

Next morning Charles was up before the sun to work on the dam. It had a two-fold purpose, he explained. Below the wall they'd have better swimming. Above he could let a canoe drift as it liked while he worked over the articles he was always being called on to write, or on mathematical problems.

"A desk is good for working, yes. But outdoors, the mind is free," he said happily. "I like to work on the dam in the cool of the day, then write or just be lazy in the afternoon."

Roy Hayden lugged stones to the dam site and the older man rolled them into place. Without seeming to, Roy managed to take on the heavier work. In the General Electric laboratory he knew Charles Steinmetz as a great man, with a heart as big as his brain.

Now he saw a different side to the little hunchback—a woodsman, a builder.

As they worked together, talk came easy. Charles felt drawn to this New England lad. He sensed a generous nature and a keen mind which only now was beginning to stir itself.

In the late afternoon a storm drove them indoors. From the cabin window, Charles watched intently as lightning flashed over the treetops and the river.

"We must tame this wild fellow or at least find a way to control him," he said, more to himself than to his companion. Never a storm came up that the scientist did not have the overpowering desire to understand this wild power of nature's.

He had probably come closer to the secret than any man who ever lived. But it was not close enough. The long power lines and stations made perfect targets for lightning. In every storm, breakdowns occurred. The wider the use of electricity, the more serious the breakdowns became. Lightning itself played havoc, but this was not the danger. The lightning often set free high voltage currents of man-made electricity.

"Between us and this terror of the skies, there is a battle royal starting. Man against

nature." Charles looked as if he were enjoying the struggle.

"Who will win?" Roy Hayden asked.

Charles smiled confidently. "Science. But
it will take us years."

# A Family for Charles

⟍ WEEK-ENDS AT THE CAMP BECAME
popular among G.E. engineers. Everyone
was expected to share in the work. Before the
year was out another room was added to the
cabin and more cots put up, so that a number
could stay overnight. But very often Roy and
Charles were left to paddle down the river
together on Sunday nights.

The older man felt a new contentment. It
was good to think aloud, to discuss a problem.
Even if Roy Hayden did not have the training
to follow the scientist's careful reasoning, he

felt he had a share in the battle that was going on against the wild fellow: lightning.

Their talk ranged far afield—about Charles' childhood in Germany, about Roy's stern and bookish upbringing in a Puritan household.

Roy introduced Charles to American books —to Emerson and Mark Twain. Charles had discovered Walt Whitman for himself. These three writers Charles called his searchlights turned on America.

"And the stars in the sky," Charles said one evening as they neared Schenectady. "These also we have in common."

But the fiery light against the horizon was not the reflection of a star! It was the glow from a fire and was coming from the direction of Liberty Street.

"I'd better hurry." Charles was tieing the boat up to the dock.

"I'll come with you." Roy ran for their bicycles under the shed and they pedaled rapidly toward the house.

A fire engine passed them, its horse team lashed to a run.

"What's on fire?" Roy called out to a passerby.

"Some backyard stable down the street. Where that crazy little hunchback lives."

As they pushed through the curious crowd that had gathered, Charles heard a man shout to his neighbor, "I always said that place would burn to the ground."

While firemen's hose kept flames under control Roy and Charles got the animals into the house and tried to salvage the equipment from the laboratory. But there was not much they could save.

The old stable burned quickly and the crowd wandered off. At last the firemen departed, too, and the two friends were alone with the wreckage.

"Look at you!" Charles said. "Your eyebrows singed off. Now Corinne will be scolding me, what I've done to her young man."

"Do you think you're better off?"

They went inside the house to clean up. "It is a big loss." Roy knew that Charles Steinmetz did as much research in his workshop at home as he did at the G.E. laboratories.

"True, quite a loss. Anyhow, I need a bigger place for my research." Charles was recovering his usual cheerfulness. "I have

been thinking anyway of building a home of
my own. I like some of that land the company has bought out near Union College. I
must build at once. I cannot be without a
lab."

He took out a sheet and began to sketch
rapidly. "This is how it will be, a two-story
building —"

"Is this your house?"

"No, the lab. We build it first. And a
place for my animals and plants. When they
are done, we start the house."

"You can certainly afford something hand-
some," Roy said. "You must have made a
fortune, growing up as you have with the
company. Think of it: 130 acres covered with
buildings in Schenectady alone, to say nothing
of the water-power station in Mechanicsville
and the smaller plants over the country. It's
a marvel, and without you it could not have
happened."

Charles Steinmetz looked at his young
friend in surprise. "I have what I need—a
living, a well-equipped laboratory, all the
assistants I ask for. G.E. has always been
generous to me. But a fortune? I have no
interest in this."

"But why?" Roy Hayden was working

hard to save money to be married. Corinne and he spent hours figuring how they could manage the little flat they had their eye on. Everyone he knew set store on money—getting ahead in the prosperous company. But here was Steinmetz, whose knowledge of electricity was the very foundation stone of their prosperity. . . . "Why?" he asked again.

"I like it that way. I know the necessity of money. I have been poor. I've sometimes gone hungry. I am happy to make a comfortable living. But more than that—a fortune? No. This is not for me."

\* \* \*

"Why is it so important where I sleep?" Charles Steinmetz asked the builder of his new home. "For me the laboratory is more important. And that my plants and animals have a roof over them."

Time was getting short. His lease on the house on Liberty Street had only a few more months to run.

"Mr. Steinmetz, houses are not built in this way. Whoever heard of putting up other buildings before the foundations of a home are laid?"

"Maybe most houses aren't." Charles answered. "But mine has to be."

The builder was trying not to lose his patience. "You are a scientist. You understand how everything must be thought out and done according to plan."

"I have a plan." Charles said calmly. "Perhaps it is a little unusual. But a very good plan. We finish the lab. And make a place for my orchids and ferns. And animals."

"But the house! What about your home?"

"All in good time. It will be a very good house, Mr. Jones. You and I, we will be proud of her. There'll not be a more livable one in all Schenectady. Now, to the plans for the lab —"

"But what about your home?"

"Mister Jones, I am as eager as you. Since a boy I have dreamed of building a place of my own. But where I sleep for the moment is unimportant." The scientist was smiling at him. "People have a way of saying I eat and sleep in my lab. For once it will be true. I'll put a cot in the upstairs room. Yes, I'll be quite comfortable there."

"I cannot build in this way. It is unheard of."

In the end Charles Steinmetz had to find another builder, then another. The laboratory finished, he moved in. The shelter for the animals was completed, and the hothouse for the plants. Still Charles delayed with the plans for his house. How could it be a real home when he lived alone?

Then, too, he was busy at the plant. The long research to control lightning was temporarily put aside. He had been asked to work on a new street lamp, an advance over the carbon lamps now in use. Charles experimented with magnetite, a black magnetized iron. The new lights would be cheaper and they gave out a steady, bluish light, easy on the eyes.

"A fine invention, Charles," Edwin Rice said.

"We'll test them out along Wendell Avenue where I live." Charles suggested.

A system of street lighting was not world-shaking like so much of his work, but bringing light to city streets gave the scientist a quiet satisfaction. Beginning in Charles' backyard, the light poles reached out into the neighborhood, a hundred and twenty-five all told.

The evening the lights were to be turned on, families along Wendell Avenue, his students from Union College, along with G.E. engineers and officials were on hand. Charles

Steinmetz threw the switch and the lights went on as far as the crowd could see. There was a moment of silence, then quick applause.

"You like it?" Charles looked around at his neighbors. "Then it is good."

He noticed that Roy Hayden had brought Corinne. A sensible, pretty girl, he thought. She will make the boy a good wife.

With the street lighting completed, Charles and his staff could give their whole attention once more to the problem of lightning. It was fast becoming a threat to the smooth working of all electric transmission lines and power stations. He began to work on a lightning-arrester. Other inventors had worked on the same problem. Even as small a thing as Bell's telephone had a lightning-arrester of a simple kind. But no one had succeeded in preventing the damage by lightning.

As Charles worked night after night, Roy came often to help, to watch, to learn.

"Why not move in with me?" Charles suggested one evening when they were working late. "There's an extra room upstairs. It will save you time and rent. And it will be company for me." Charles smiled shyly. "You know how I am. I do not enjoy living alone. Since we are working together, I can cook for both of us. It will be practical all around."

"Thanks. I will be glad to." Roy said, understanding the older man's kindness and realizing how lonely he was. "I'll stay tonight and next week I'll give up my room across town."

Charles promptly began planning his house again. With his usual energy, he set builders to work. The foundations and framework were done before cold weather set in. Before the first snow fell, the roof was on. The work went forward all winter.

However, Charles kept changing the plans for the rooms. It was not like him to be uncertain of what he wanted, but he was building this splendid house of many rooms without knowing who was going to live in it. Without a family, a house was not a home.

Roy and Corinne would be married in the spring. They had already found a small flat. Charles could not help comparing their enthusiasm with his own uncertainty.

Long ago he had made up his mind never to marry. Only once in his thirty-six years had his determination weakened. There had been a moment—how many years ago? It was that lonely year when Mr. Eickemeyer retired. At his first job for General Electric, in Lynn, Massachusetts. . . . He had begun work for G.E., in 1893. It was now 1901. Was it possible that eight years had gone by?

Charles went to his desk and fumbled through folders of pictures. His camera had been a new toy in Lynn. He had taken it with him everywhere and the young girl next door to his boardinghouse had made a good subject. That was how it had begun.

Yes, here was the first picture. Julia with her long braids hanging down, sitting primly on her doorstep. Julia playing for him by the window on her piano. Julia on the boatride with her parents. Julia with her arms around the puppy he gave her.

Julia was only sixteen—but perhaps this gentle, thoughtful girl, as she grew to womanhood, might overlook his deformity. Julia might come to love him. He would have patience. His work, his life had taught him patience. He told no one, least of all Julia herself.

Suddenly, she had fallen ill. . . . Charles looked for a long time at the last picture he had taken of Julia. She was in the hospital. Such a longing in her eyes. He never told her how he felt. But she knew. And there was comfort in it, when she was gone.

Gently, Charles fitted the faded pictures back into the folder. He was facing one of the big decisions of his life and he was not ready for it. The memory of Julia, whose name he had never mentioned to anyone, was a help in making up his mind.

The house was finished in June. As fine a place as in all Schenectady, but empty. Charles continued to live in the room over the lab even after Roy Hayden left to be married.

Charles could not be at the wedding. He was in Massachusetts, receiving an honorary degree from Harvard: "Charles P. Steinmetz, the leading engineer in America."

Other honors had come to him that spring. He had been elected President of the American Institute of Electrical Engineers. And he was going to teach a class at Union College. He would enjoy this. Young people were the future. And he had been appointed to the School Board of the city. He was making his life count.

When he returned from Harvard, Roy Hayden was already back from his wedding trip. The younger man jumped up and came over to Charles' desk. "Congratulations on your honorary degree!" he said. "How did you like Harvard?"

"Congratulations, yourself. How is Co-rinne? How did you like Niagara Falls?"

That evening, while Corinne and Roy were having supper, there was a knock on their door.

"Why, come in! You are our first guest." The young people made the famous scientist welcome.

"I was in the neighborhood and dropped by," Charles began, then looked at them with a quick, shy grin. "The truth is, I wanted to see you. Corinne has never examined my house. I thought maybe we could walk over together to see it."

*Their first evening at home and they had all the wedding presents to unpack and the furniture to arrange.* Roy hesitated, but Corinne said quickly, "Of course. We'd like to, very much."

On the way over, Charles chatted about everything except what was on his mind. But, as they came in sight of the house, he fell silent. Every room had been lighted, and without speaking he led the way from empty room to empty room.

"It is a lovely house, Mr. Steinmetz," Corinne said. She admired the wide hall with its fine woodwork and the spacious rooms.

"I am a little fellow for such a big place, eh?" Charles looked from her to Roy. Then he blurted out, "Why not come here and live?"

Roy was looking at Corinne. "It is generous of you, Charles. But —"

"Hear me out. We will make a family. Roy knows he is like a son to me, even if I am a little young to be his father. We can make a good life together. For us. And for your children." He put his hand on Roy's shoulder, "I am going down to look to my plants and animals for the night. That will give you time to talk it over."

When he returned, they met him in the hallway.

"We accept," Roy said.

Corinne's eyes were red. "Don't mind me. I always cry when I'm happy. You will have to get used to a woman's ways around the house, Mr. Steinmetz. I warn you, I'm bossy."

Charles laughed. "And you'll find me a nuisance."

"You! Oh, I admit I've heard of your chemicals and the stains on everything. I am a strict housekeeper. No burns on the carpet!"

"Only a few."

"And one final condition."

"What?"   Charles was anxious.

Corinne leaned over and kissed him lightly on the cheek.   "That you let me call you Dad."

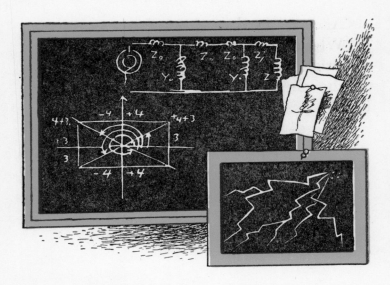

# The Lightning Maker

 "ARE YOU BUSY, GRANDDAD?" Joe Hayden stuck a tousled head through the door of Charles Steinmetz' study.

"Come in, Joe. This is Dr. Einstein, from my old school in Zurich."

"Hello!" The boy glanced at the visitor with a friendly, passing interest. Granddad had so many visitors. Some of them were famous and important, like Mr. Edison who made the new phonograph in their parlor, or Mr. Ford who made automobiles. Some, like the tall, dark man named Marconi, could not speak English, but Granddad could talk with him. This stranger with the bushy hair and merry eyes was saying something in a foreign language, too, and Granddad was answering with a grin a mile wide.

His grandfather liked having visitors, but no matter who was in the study Joe knew that he was welcome. Sometimes Mom was too busy with housework and Dad had his nose in a book, but Granddad never said, "Come later." He always had time for questions—even the silly ones Midge or Billy asked.

"Excuse me a moment, Dr. Einstein?" Charles Steinmetz turned to his grandson. "Did you want to ask me something, Joe?"

"Well," Joe looked at the visitor. "It's a secret, you know."

"You can trust Albert Einstein with secrets. He knows a few himself."

"About what?"

"About the universe."

"Oh. Mine's about Billy's birthday. Can we have fireworks? I told Pete Lamson you could make real firecrackers. He doesn't believe me. The rest of the gang do. They say you can do magic."

"And you—what do you think, young man?" Albert Einstein asked in broken English.

"I think my grandfather is like everybody else. He's no different."

"You see, Dr. Einstein, my family knows me better than the great public." Charles glanced up with open pride at his grandson. "Yes," he said. "We'll have real fireworks. And now go tell your mother that Dr. Einstein will stay for lunch."

As the door closed, Albert Einstein asked, "How old is your adopted grandson?"

"Joe is almost fourteen. As you see, he is already taller than I. There is also Midge, a bright piece. Billy will be eight. He is the birthday child." Charles, his eyes twinkling, said, "I too have a secret. Wait, I will show you."

He pulled a box from under his desk and began to untie it. "Lock the door," he said mysteriously.

Ten minutes later Charles and the young scientist from across the ocean were on the floor watching a small electric train going round and round its track.

"I had a steam train when I was a boy," Charles said softly. "Now I have made this for Billy."

"When I go back to the Polytechnic School in Zurich," Albert Einstein teased, "I shall tell them that the electrical genius they are so proud of spends his time on the floor playing with toys."

"You dare not." Charles was laughing. "Because you would have to confess that their famous Doctor Einstein was equally anxious for a turn at running the train!"

After lunch, Charles Steinmetz took his visitor to the railroad station, then hurried to the G.E. plant. A group of his students from Union College were waiting to see the latest model of the lightning arrester.

In the last years the damage from lightning had grown alarmingly. Steinmetz had designed several "sentinels" to guard power systems. So far, none had been wholly successful. Breakdowns in power plants were still reported after every storm.

There was great interest in this newest "sentinel" though no one could tell, until it was tried out, whether it would be better than the others.

"The principle of a lightning-arrester is quite simple." Charles explained. "We take advantage of lightning's one weakness: its habit of going whichever way is easiest to take. It follows the line of least resistance, like a white mouse in a maze.

"Old Ben Franklin took advantage of this same weakness when, a hundred and thirty years ago, he invented the lightning rod. But Franklin didn't have high voltage power systems to contend with! In an electric system, lightning is the troublemaker. But the real damage is done by the current itself, set free from its circuit by the lightning bolt.

"This power breaks loose when lightning strikes. It goes wild," the scientist continued. "The arrester's first job is to open a path for the bolt to pass into the ground. Then it must keep the current running along the transmission lines. When the arrester works, electric power keeps on its way to serve man's needs. The whole drama of clash and counter-clash of unseen forces is over so fast that people using electric power never know what is happening."

"Wonderful!" The students said as they examined the model.

"Not wonderful, but necessary." Steinmetz told them. "It is still not perfect and there is too much guesswork. 'Try and fail, and try again' has gone on for too many years. What is needed is to bring lightning itself into the laboratory, to see how the old fellow works! Then we could test the arresters as they are built."

"But who could make lightning?" a student asked, and the others laughed.

One, shrewder than the rest, kept his eyes on Steinmetz. "Are you working on such a machine?" he asked.

Charles hesitated. "I have worked on the problem for I don't know how many years. I have not succeeded in making lightning."

The students were still asking questions when a messenger came over from the office.

"A long distance call for you, Dr. Steinmetz. The man says he is a farmer who lives near your camp. He said if you were busy he would talk with Mr. Hayden."

At a nod from Steinmetz, Roy Hayden went out to take the call and the scientist went on with his explanation. However, when Roy appeared again in the doorway, Charles called out anxiously, "Come, come! What is it?"

Roy was thinking how to break the news. For so many years Camp Mohawk had been the great joy of their free hours. "There was a bad storm at Viele Creek last night," he began. "Rain and lightning."

"Lightning?"

"It is rather bad news, Dad. Lightning struck the cabin—"

Charles jumped to his feet. "It *struck?*" He was pulling on his jacket. "It's a rare piece of luck!" He looked around for his camera. "Will you excuse me, gentlemen? Roy, will you drive me out there before anything is touched? Think of it! We are handed a chance in a million to study at first hand how lightning works."

At camp they found "the terror of the skies" had put on quite an act. Traveling down a tree near the camp, then leaping to the cabin, the lightning had divided into two forks. One passed into the ground along one of the cabin's supporting timbers, throwing off large splinters as it passed.

The other fork of lightning had smashed a window, hit the camp's lighting circuit, then split into several directions, tearing or shattering everything it touched. In the bedroom it had jumped from a loose end of wire to a looking glass, and from there to the ground. Splinters from the mirror were thrown as far as twenty feet.

"Roy, help me collect these glass splinters," he said. "This proves the explosive power of a bolt of lightning—something we had not taken enough into account. This mirror is our most important piece of evidence against the outlaw."

Roy thought it impossible to put the hundreds of glass fragments together. Toward midnight he said, "I was never good at jigsaw puzzles," and gave up and went to bed.

Charles worked through the night. For days he kept at it until he had every piece in place. He sent for large plates of glass, sealed the re-made mirror between them and took it to the G.E. laboratory.

"Now at last we are beginning to understand lightning," he said.

\*       \*       \*

Months later, in the winter of 1922, reporters from a dozen newspapers crowded around Charles Steinmetz in a corner of the big laboratory. They had come to see the workings of a mysterious, new machine.

It looked quite ordinary: just two large wooden racks holding two hundred coated glass plates and a network of wires.

"These glass plates are our thunderclouds," the scientist explained. "Like the thunderclouds, these condensers store up electric current, bit by bit. When they have stored as much as they can take, they behave like the thundercloud. They discharge their electric force through the line of least resistance. The result, a flash of lightning."

He touched a switch. There was a hum that seemed louder to the waiting men than it was. Suddenly, with a thunderous crack, a bolt of lightning darted from the machine.

The newspaper men shrank back as if they had been struck. The terrific flash was followed by a sharp, acrid smell. The very air seemed to be alive with electricity. The men cried out in tense, nervous voices, as if they were indeed in the center of a storm.

Another crack like a pistol shot! And another!

One bolt crumpled a piece of heavy wire to dust, another consumed a block of wood.

Charles was enjoying himself. He had the limb of a tree brought into the laboratory. With a bolt of lightning he destroyed the living branch.

"Compared to natural lightning, this is on a small scale," Steinmetz said quietly, as soon as he could be heard above the excited clamor. "Nature's bolt has five hundred times the energy: a million volts here in the laboratory, five hundred million in the sky."

Nevertheless, it was real lightning that the

scientist had made.    Word of the machine was front page news.

The reporters pictured Charles Steinmetz as the "Wizard of Schenectady," as "Jove throwing his thunderbolts around the laboratory as a boy might toss balls."

"A lot of poppycock," Charles said, when the whole family came to his study next morning waving the newspapers.    "The machine will help me design a more perfect lightning arrester.    That is all."

He was annoyed.    He had done other, more important work.    These solid accomplishments had not brought forth a lot of nonsense. *Jove. Wizard. Giant.*    He did not like to be raised above ordinary men and set apart.

"That's what comes of playing magic, Granddad," Joe said.    "Now the gang will never believe me when I tell 'em you're no different from anyone else."

"No different!"    Joe's mother laughed. "Look at the headlines—and the batch of telegrams.    And the telephone ringing all morning so I couldn't get my housework done! Your grandfather will just have to put up with it, Joe.    The whole world knows he is a magician."

*            *            *

Charles Steinmetz *was* able to work magic —the magic of science. Today, the huge turbines and generators from Niagara in the East to Boulder Dam in the West are proof of it. And, on the top of the Empire State building in New York, the first-hand study of lightning goes on. One hundred and two stories up, where the "outlaw" strikes oftenest, Nature furnishes an outdoor laboratory, such as Steinmetz would have gloried in.

Here, younger men carry on the "battle royal" against destructive forces—sure, because of the little giant's leadership, that Man will win.

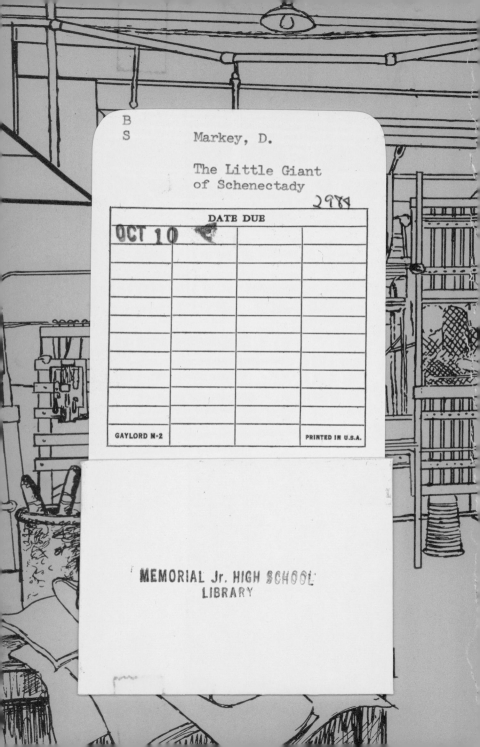

B
S

Markey, D.

The Little Giant
of Schenectady

2984